CLIFF WILKERSON
Siri Doesn't Tango
AND OTHER STORIES

Copyrighted Material

Siri Doesn't Tango and Other stories

Copyright © 2020 by Cliff Wilkerson.
All Rights Reserved.

No part of this publication may be reproduced, stored in a retrieval system or transmitted, in any form or by any means—electronic, mechanical, photocopying, recording or otherwise—without prior written permission from the publisher, except for the inclusion of brief quotations in a review.

For information about this title or to order other books and/ or electronic media, contact the publisher:

Douglas C. Wilkerson, M. D.
dcwilkerson0654@sbcglobal.net

Library of Congress Control Number: 2020901949

ISBNs
978-1-7341600-0-0 (print)
978-1-7341600-1-7 (eBook)

Printed in the United States of America

Cover design: Bruce Wilkerson

Interior design: 1106 Design

*To the many loved ones who no longer
bless my life with their presence.*

CONTENTS

Acknowledgments ix

Vampires Never Play 1

The Man With the Knife 19

Sugarfoot 29

Gassing Up 39

Memories of Ruth 49

The Gypsy 65

The Woman in the Mirror 79

Tennessee Man 97

Lot's Wife 103

Bird Tales 109

Small Town Guy   115

Snakes   127

Growing Snakes   133

Beheading a Snake   137

Cat Island   143

Family Entertainment   163

Thumbing It   181

A Plumbing Odyssey   183

Breakneck Speed   197

Don't be Foolish, Old Man   209

Driving to Tango with Siri   219

Two Angels in the Night   233

Author Bio   241

ACKNOWLEDGMENTS

I want to thank all of my family and friends, as well as strangers, who enriched my life with their stories or had interesting exchanges with me that stimulated the telling of a story. I have changed the names of many of the characters in these stories, and I also took creative license with all those that came from friends and strangers. The memoirs I tried to write as truthfully as my memory allowed.

I am truly fortunate to have a creative son who teaches, dances, paints, and writes and who worked diligently to fashion the cover for my book. To you, Bruce, I give a special thanks.

Thanks, too, to my son, Scott, who has been unfailing in his support of me through the hardships of advancing "maturity" and all else that moving into the winter of life brings.

I also want to thank Eva Sandburg who carefully read through the manuscript and made necessary corrections and helpful suggestions.

To my niece and nephew, Carol and Larry Barkan, who unfailingly read my stories and encouraged me with their loving responses to my efforts, I owe thanks.

Barbara Baumbell, who was my first real date and with whom I became reacquainted seventy years later. When she learned that I'd written about that event, she has since read all three of my published books, much that I haven't published, and every story in this volume. She still asks for more. Thanks, Barbara, for being one of my most faithful readers.

And most of all I want to thank my late wife, Carolyn, to whom I was married for over sixty years. She has some presence in many of these stories and thoughts of her are a reminder of good things in my life that I have, or haven't, written about.

VAMPIRES NEVER PLAY

It was a quiet Sunday afternoon; the sun was warm and I was comfortably reclined in my backyard deck chair reading Michael Ondaatje's *The Cat's Table*. From time to time I looked up to admire the late summer blooms that emerge each season without my having more to do than watch and wait for them—and enjoy. When the doorbell rang, disturbing my self-indulged tranquility, I grumbled to myself, "It best not be another spritely, smiling widow with a batch of cookies." I stomped through my living room to the front door and when I pulled it open, realized that seeing a widow would have been welcome. Standing there was Gloria, my drug-addicted, twenty-two-year-old step-granddaughter and her son, Alfie, who wasn't yet old enough to be in first grade.

"Hi, Grandpa Jack," she gushed, then threw her arms around my neck and squeezed till my arthritic neck-bones crackled like heated popcorn. "We just drove in from Southern California and we just couldn't wait to see you, could we, Alfie?"

Alfie stood silent, owlishly staring at me until his mother said, with a note of warning in her voice, "Alfie?" The boy nodded but said nothing.

I stood there for several beats, not wanting to invite them in. But I couldn't ask her to leave. Reluctant but resigned, I invited them in. Gloria only showed up when she wanted something and I wasn't in a giving mood.

"You look great, Grandpa."

For a sixty-six-year-old, bald man with a face creased with sorrow and sporting a turkey wattle, I thought. Not to mention ten or so pounds overweight from eating fast foods for a year. "Yeah," I said. "Comes from clean living."

Gloria frowned but quickly exchanged it for a giggle. Barely seated in the kitchen with a cup of tea in her hand, she asked, "Grandpa Jack, would you please, please look after Alfie for a couple of days?" Pleading with her eyes, she continued, "I've a job prospect in Peoria. I can't take Alfie with me. Please, please keep him company till I see about the position." I noticed her cup trembled against the saucer, rhythmically clicking before she could bring it to her thin, bloodless lips, and I wondered if she was high on something.

"I want to go to my Grandma Gwen's," Alfie piped up. Barely five years old, he reminded me of a small, professorial leprechaun with his shiny red hair, light-skinned complexion sprinkled with freckles, and green eyes framed in tortoiseshell glasses too large on such a small face. "She takes good care of me."

Nodding my approval of his good sense, I said, "I think she could take better care of him."

"Grandpa Jack, you know very well that mother has lung cancer. She can't even get out of bed without help. You know that, too, Alfie."

Alfie glared at his Dr. Pepper, but said nothing, unwilling to cede the point to his mother.

From the minute I married Beth, my stepdaughter, Gwen, disliked me and made no secret of it. Now, forty-one years later, she still chose to have little or nothing to do with me and hadn't spoken in the year since Beth had passed on. I knew she had cancer but not how ill she was.

"I'm sorry about your mother," I said. "But, what about your dad? He's retired on disability, I know. But he gets around okay."

"It's all Daddy can do just to take care of Mom. And he's gotten worse in the last six months. I can't ask him."

"What about Alfie's father?"

"What about him?"

"Can't he take Alfie?"

"Dad's in Canada," Alfie said.

With some other woman, I thought. Or the bill collectors are after him.

"Dan hasn't been around for two years and, besides, he's too fond of you know what to look after his son."

And so are you, I thought. I recalled now that Alfie had learned how to dial the telephone when he was not even three yet. Learned the different tones of the phone even though he couldn't read the numbers. Would call Beth to come get him when his mom or dad were too far gone on drugs to feed him, and she would bring him home and take care of him. But he wanted no part of Alfie or his mother.

"His parents?"

"They can't even take care of their cat. How are they going to take care of Alfie?"

"I don't know how to take care of little boys," I protested.

"I can take care of myself." Alfie's eyes brightened with indignation. "At my grandma Gwen's." He downed half the glass of Dr. Pepper

I'd set before him, then turned bright red as he tried to suppress a burp. Couldn't.

Gloria gave her son a distracted look and shook her head, frizzy blond hair, long and poorly trimmed, swirling about her face. "No, Alfie. Like I said, Grandma is too ill right now. You need to stay with Grandpa Jack."

I glared at her but could come up with no other excuse to refuse Alfie. "How long?"

"Just a day or two. He's been with you before, when Granny Beth was alive."

I really didn't want to think about that, Beth being alive. It was too painful a thought because she was passed on. Having Alfie here would be a daily reminder as well. "Just for a day or two?"

"I promise."

"Okay. But, just a day or two," I insisted, knowing full well this wasn't a good idea. To Gloria just a day or two might mean a week or two.

"Thanks, Grandpa Jack. I really owe you. I'll see about this job in Peoria, get us an apartment, and be back by tomorrow night or Tuesday at the latest." Gloria drank the rest of her tea in one gulp, threw me an air kiss, hugged Alfie, told him to be a good boy, and flew out the door. Taking a suitcase and backpack from the car she ran back and deposited it on the porch and sprinted back as if I were in pursuit to give both boy and suitcase back. Alfie and I watched her drive away, then I stooped and hefted the suitcase and carried it into the living room, Alfie dragging his backpack behind looking as though he'd bitten into a sour lemon.

It was awkward, us standing on the green carpet that covers most of my downstairs, me feeling resentful and out of my depth, Alfie studying me with his wide, greenish, owl's eyes and waiting, I suspected, for me to make the first move. "Look, Alfie, I really like you. It's just I don't know much about . . ." I trailed off. I'd already said I didn't know how to take care of little boys. "Let's take a walk."

He said nothing, just nodded, and hefted his oversize backpack onto his shouders.

I led Alfie to the park, and sat with him on a bench watching some little league baseballers swat endlessly and unsuccessfully at lightly thrown hardballs. He'd dragged along the backpack which was two sizes too large for someone so young to manage and had insisted I not help him. Perching himself on the edge of the bench at a respectful distance from me, he sat swinging one leg back and forth as he buried his nose in a book. When the crowd of parents roared, sometimes encouragingly and at others in a mean-spirited manner that should have shamed them, he looked up for a moment. I thought I detected a disdainful glance when one of the six-year-olds connected solidly with a ball, sending it into the outfield, then jumping in joy when he dashed across home plate.

"You already missing your mom?" I asked.

Looking up at me with serious eyes, he shook his head, then buried himself in the book once more.

Thinking I was unobserved, I glanced sideways at the title.

"It's a math workbook," Alfie said.

Impressed that he was smart enough to do math at his age, but embarrassed that he caught me being nosy, I took a feigned interest in the progress of the game and thought about what Beth had told me of this child before she passed away, leaving me a widower. During his first two years, Alfie lived with Gloria, his irresponsible mother, who spent much of her time high on dope and who left him alone in his crib for long periods. Rarely present, his father was either lost in his own marijuana-induced private world or living with some other woman. Had Alfie not periodically been taken in by my Beth, no telling what would have become of him. Those times he was with

Beth and me, I'd had little to do with him. Divorced from my first wife partly because of her nagging insistence on having children and while married to Beth barely tolerating Gloria until she left for college, I had been somewhat intolerant of Alfie's presence. Were Beth alive right now, I'd not complain a bit. But with her gone, here I was being saddled with this despondent five-year-old and, the ball game over, not knowing what next to do. I supposed offering food would be a good start.

Back at the house I fed Alfie a dinner of hot dogs, cold potato salad, cookies, and chocolate ice cream, a meal I knew Beth would not approve. He was quiet and I could think of nothing to say after I tried recapping the ball game only to be met with baleful stares and finally the comment, "I don't really like baseball." At bedtime I showed him the spare bedroom where, while ignoring me as I stood shifting from one foot to another, not knowing my role in this bedtime ritual, he opened his small suitcase and took a pair of pajamas covered with trains of all description, donned them in silence, crawled into bed, and fell asleep with the light still on and me standing where I'd been wearing a hole in the carpet. I probably should have mentioned a bath, or brushing his teeth, but that only occurred to me after his breathing softened into sleep. I was relieved he was out for the night.

I took Monday and Tuesday off from work, something I hated to do, needing as I did the certainty of going into an office and burying myself in the safety of my work. Seeing patients took my mind off my worries. Alfie kept his nose in a book, though I noticed that he did not often turn the pages, and I wondered if he was faking it. When I turned on TV cartoons, he turned his back on the screen. I read the newspaper, watched talk shows, and waited with growing aggravation for word from Gloria. For meals, we mostly made trips out to the nearest fast-food restaurants where I ordered us Pancake

House pancakes, Kentucky Fried Chicken meals, Burger King Whoppers, Taco Bell tamales. There seemed to be nothing wrong with his appetite. We had ice cream at home.

When I hadn't heard from Gloria by late Tuesday night, I arranged through my Polish housekeeper to employ her friend Marie to stay with Alfie while I went into work. Marie was horrified at my suggestion to take Alfie out to Burger King for lunch, so I gave her money to go grocery shopping and buy what she thought best for a five-year-old boy. Days passed and Gloria neither called nor showed her face. Her mother wouldn't, or couldn't, tell me where Gloria was holed up. Her father refused to even think of Alfie coming to stay with them; he had less tolerance for young boys than I did.

Alfie and I were on our own for the weekend.

Well, not for long. The doorbell rang just before lunchtime on Saturday and, when I opened the door, the widow-woman Linda Gentry stood there smiling and thrusting out a tray covered with a bright blue cloth on which pink flowers curled and seemed ready to burst forth from their tightly threaded moorings. She was dressed in a jogging outfit, and had tied her gray hair back in a ponytail. Her blue eyes sparkled with a hint of amusement, I suspect, at the poleaxed stare I greeted her with.

"Hello, Jack," she said. "Marie told me what wretched meals you and Alfie might suffer over the weekend when she isn't here, and I thought you might enjoy some of the beef roast and fresh baked bread I made."

I was speechless. And, I thought afterward, a bit rude, as I could only stutter, "Th-th-thanks, Linda. You shouldn't have." I did not invite her in.

The silence that followed went on much too long before she said, "That's quite all right. You can bring the dishes back anytime." She gave me another smile and jogged away.

She was a tall woman of fifty-seven who kept herself fit running a mile every day, and I couldn't help but admire her as she zipped away, her gray ponytail bobbing left and right, but then a forceful image of Beth with her more matronly figure and soft edges quickly giving me a hurt stare chased those admiring thoughts away and I hurried to put the food on the table. I was so shaken by the encounter that my hands shook, and I was afraid I'd drop the tray.

When I reached the kitchen, I discovered Linda had failed to mention the cherry cobbler she'd included. I felt another stab of pain; that was Beth's favorite. To distract myself, I called Alfie to the table early. He eyed the meal suspiciously. "Did you cook this?"

"No, a lady, Ms. Gentry, did."

He nodded. "She makes really good cookies, too. Better even than Marie's."

"You know her?"

"Yea, Marie and I visit her every day."

I was going to have to talk to Marie about encouraging Linda to focus attention on Alfie. Or on me. The image of Beth that Linda's visit had conjured left me a little shaky.

That thought reminded me that Beth had bought toys for Alfie, and that I hadn't yet discarded them. I dug around in the garage where a box had lain moldering for over a year and found some little cars, Elmer's glue, different colored paper, a ball of thick string, wooden blocks, a bag of marbles, crayons, and masking tape. When I showed them to Alfie, he ignored most of the contents, choosing only the paper and a pencil which he used to begin writing down what he called his "plans," none of which he showed me.

When on Monday I arrived home from work, I was met with Marie's complaint, "Alfie's much too serious. He won't play and refuses to talk about his family or friends. He won't even go outside and play by himself."

I could only shrug my shoulders, displaying my ignorance of what to do.

"He will go down to visit Linda Gentry's, though, won't he?" I said, a bit of accusation spicing my question.

"Alfie likes her."

He only brightens up when I tell him we're going over to Linda's house. He loves her cookies."

"But is it a good idea to bring her into this?" I said, still shaken by the widow's appearance at my door.

"I don't see why not. And it's a break for me to visit with her." There was a note of defiance in Marie's tone.

Chastened, I could only rejoin with a weak, "Oh, I see. Well. Great." Nothing more was said of Linda and that week ended with no word from Gloria.

I dreaded the upcoming weekend without work or Marie, and the fact that I had to resort to fast foods again until Monday. Thanks to Linda and Marie, meals had improved greatly; rich lamb stew, roasted chicken, vegetables, which I never bothered with, and homemade pies, cakes, and chocolate puddings. I prayed, though, that Gloria would drive up by Friday night's end. No luck there and the two-day weekend was spent mostly in pained silence. However, on Sunday evening Alfie looked up from his "plans" and said, "Aren't I supposed to be in school?"

"School?" I hadn't given that a thought, believing Gloria would return any day now.

"Uh-huh. School. I was in preschool some of the time last year."

"Yes, I suppose you should be in school," I said, then realized what an awful admission I'd just made. Alfie could be here indefinitely. The walls seemed to close in on me, and my face suffused with heat. I wanted to utter a string of curse words, but, with that small boy present, I let them build inside until my head came near exploding.

I took part of a day off on Monday and enrolled Alfie in a nearby private kindergarten, deciding that would be better than trying to get him into public school when I had no papers showing he was in my charge. I hated to part with the money, but I could afford it. I arranged for Marie to get him to school, pick him up, and fix something for our dinner. After his first day, we had finished a tasty meal of baked chicken, potatoes, green beans, and apple pie; a meal more to my tastes than to Alfie's. We sat opposite one another across the kitchen table while I read about the latest casualties in our latest nonwar conflict, and Alfie worked on his "plan." After a few minutes I looked up from my paper and saw that Alfie had dropped his head to the table.

"What's wrong?" I inquired.

"Nothing, I'm just tired." He fidgeted a moment and asked "How much time do we have left till bedtime?" His eyes were glistening with tears.

"Not long," I said. "Is there something wrong?" He would not talk about his mother, even though I'd brought the subject up a few times, but I figured he was pining for her.

"No," Alfie countered, "I'm just thinking about my plan."

"Could you tell me about it?"

"No, it's a private plan and I have to work it out." Alfie laid his head back down, closed his eyes, and fell fast asleep.

I carried him to bed, his warm little body pressed close to my chest. It felt strangely comforting and I held him for a moment before I laid him down, pulled off his shoes and covered him, still clothed. There was a lump in my throat and the face of Beth floated into my head. I'd not held anyone close since she'd passed on. Tears came and I gouged them away with my knuckles. I hadn't cried at the funeral and I did not want to do so now. I hurried out of the room, turned on Fox News, and forced all other thoughts from my mind.

For the next several evenings after dinner, Alfie continued to work on his plan for a while and then rested his head on the table. When I would suggest that he appeared to be sleepy and perhaps should go to bed, he insisted that was not so; it was only that he could think better with his eyes closed. One night I mentioned that he looked sad and tears sprang to his eyes and he turned away from me. Matter-of-factly, he said, "I was very busy in school today." Each night he would fall asleep moments after taking out paper and pencil, leaving it for me to carry him off to bed. Each night as I again felt his little warm body close to me, I would think of Beth and be close to tears.

Then, one evening he mashed his left small finger when closing the door to the kitchen and became quite upset. "I don't want to live here anymore," he said through his tears. "There's nothing to do and we just sit around." Crying and upset, he went to his room, where he stayed the rest of the evening. I found myself regretting that I'd not been able to carry him to bed.

As days passed, I became miserable over his unhappiness. The housekeeper said he was better with her, and in a meeting with his teacher at school, she said he was doing well, that he was a very bright boy, and worked very diligently at his desk. I suspected she was one of those teachers who valued a working child more than one who played.

The evening after I met with his teacher, as I sat with Alfie, I grew sleepy, feeling as if I were spaced out, strange feelings to have been stirred up by a small boy. He fell asleep and I carried him to bed, feeling the close warmth of him, the little-boy smell; a mixture of young sweat and of the steak he had eaten that evening after dumping half a bottle of ketchup on it. When I laid him down, I felt, as I had each time I'd carried him to bed, a deep sadness. Except, this time I could no longer hold back the tears. Rushing from the room to my bedroom, I threw myself on the bed and wept. When I awoke six hours later, still fully clothed, the moon was streaming in my window. Beth and

I used to lie in this same bed and watch the moon when it was full and wandering past. Then, the realization came that I felt calmer and more at peace than I had since her death. She had loved her little great-grandson, had cried when Gloria whisked him away to California and she couldn't cuddle him anymore. She'd never seen him again. Here he was back in her house, but such a sad little boy.

One evening a few days later I asked Alfie about what he'd done at school that day: if he had played with anyone.

Alfie looked at me very solemnly and said, "I am a vampire, one of the living dead. And, vampires are not allowed to play."

I was thunderstruck.

Astounded at this admission, I scarcely knew what to do. Take him to a therapist? A psychiatrist? Just listen and hope it was a game he was playing and not worry so? Ignore it? I called a colleague of mine, Dr. Tony Dullas, a well-respected pediatrician, who examined Alfie and declared him quite normal. "Fantasies are not uncommon in this aged child," he said, dismissively.

In the days that followed, Alfie bit my tables, couch, television, chairs, ottoman, and all the other pieces of furniture in my house, thereby transforming them into vampires. My rug, my drapes, my walls all became vampires. Only I was spared, though on one weekend day with great solemnity he told me. "If you want to be grandpa to a vampire, you have to become one." It was the first time I'd had even a glimmer that he might consider me kin, and it so surprised me that I agreed but suggest perhaps if he bit my shirt, that might be sufficient to infect me. After a moment of silent deliberation, he ceremoniously bit down on my cuff.

As I thought about his inclusion of me into his vampire life, I was troubled that it might be one more nail in the coffin of my responsibility to keep Alfie. He was pulling me into a way of life I was loath to follow. I caught myself thinking that my vampire step-great-grandson, who had pressed his vampire mark on my person and furnishings was enslaving me. Though it was my shirt he'd bitten, it seemed as if my skin really was wearing those twin marks now evident on so many things in my home. Now he was deadening my attention with that inner biting conviction of his. The sense of deadness from which he suffered was having a profound effect upon me.

I'm not sure how this dead time would have ended if, while turning into my driveway on a Wednesday afternoon, I had not come within an inch of flattening Linda as she jogged around the corner and onto my drive. I screeched to a halt, the seat belt digging into my shoulder. Linda pounded on the hood once with the flat of her hand, then flashed me a smile.

"We have to quit running into each other this way," she quipped as I jumped out of the car to give my apologies.

"Linda, are you all right? I'm sorry. Really sorry. I was preoccupied."

"I'm fine." She wiped sweat from her face with a towel pulled from the back of her lavender jogging suit, then fanned herself with it. "How's our little vampire doing?"

My face crimsoned. "You know about that?"

"I think it's kind of cute. We've been talking about him dressing up as Count Dracula for Halloween."

"Should we be encouraging that?"

She shook her head. "No. But we sure can't ignore it. That's who he is right now. That's about all he will talk about."

I shrugged. That was true. "It's getting to me, though. I'm beginning to worry he's actually turned me into one of the living dead who can't have any fun."

Linda laughed. "From what I've noticed, you don't seem to get out and have much fun, anyway." She blushed then. "I'm sorry. I know you lost Beth only a year ago. But Alfie needs you to encourage him to have fun. Take him out. Do some fun things."

I felt criticized and angry, though I realized she was right. "Listen, Linda, I've got to get inside and let Marie take off. Thanks for the advice."

"Any time, Jack. Just call."

As she ran on, I stood watching her strong legs moving smoothly along the ground, admiring her again, and though Beth came to mind, I did not feel the same shakiness I'd experienced earlier. Linda was right about me not having fun. Beth would not have wanted that. I decided I should make more of an effort to be friendly to Linda, and to take her advice about having fun. With Alfie.

I began insisting that Alfie and I try new things, go to a movie, to the park, or to a museum, saying I wanted to teach him to have fun. He kept insisting that vampires did not have fun, only worked, and that I wasn't being a good vampire. He showed little enjoyment going out with me, but objected less and less.

During all this time, I kept expressing amazement that he and his imaginary companions, all vampires, were never permitted any fun until one day he turned to me in exasperation.

"It is a rule of the committee," he told me. "And they're thinking of not letting you be a vampire anymore. You like to play too much."

That was a new development. I had not before heard of this ruling body that governed Alfie's world. In the days that followed, I learned that the rules committee which laid down the laws governing vampire behavior was a strict body. They were harsh in their punishment. There was no way they would deign to discuss the edicts they laid down even though, time and again, I tried to get Alfie to initiate a discussion with them. I decided to defy their edicts and attempted even more to be playful. I was informed one day on the way to a movie that I was no longer a vampire. I have to say I was not disappointed though I worried Alfie might pull further away from me.

One day, after I'd cut my thumb trying to prepare a fresh mango and had to apply a bandage, I tried to engage Alfie in a brief, teasing word game. "Look up," I said and Alfie looked up. "Now look down." He complied again. "Now look at my thumb." He did. "Isn't it dumb?" I asked, laughing then at my own humor. After giving me what looked to be a half-smile, Alfie's looks became stern.

"Grandpa, you have to remember that vampires never like jokes. They just like work."

I was thrilled that for the first time he'd actually called me Grandpa. And, I was pleased that I had seen a half smile play across his lips for a fleeting moment before he reprimanded me. That smile gave me hope that he had not totally committed himself to the gloom of a living death spent working and sucking blood.

Several days had passed during which I was in conflict with the committee when, on a Sunday afternoon, as I sat at my desk writing, Alfie came to me and said, "I want you to meet Roquefort. He gets dirty crawling around on your floor like a baby and the committee hates that."

I thought my floors were fairly respectable and clean especially since our housekeeper was here so often. I said so to Alfie.

"Well, it's there and vampires can't stand dirt. And Roquefort is very dirty."

I took a sip of my now tepid coffee and asked, "I suppose he's getting into a lot of trouble with the committee?"

"Un-huh. He's always belching and he farts a lot, too."

"Goodness, that could be annoying to a vampire," I said.

"He talks back and can't do what he's supposed to, even when he knows the rules. And he wants to play. I have to keep an eye on him."

"I should think it normal that very young vampires would act that way," I said. "Young humans do."

"Not vampire babies. Roquefort gets a beating every time the committee finds out he's been playing."

"But he's a baby!" I cried.

"He knows the rules," Alfie said, and ended the conversation.

Roquefort became a permanent resident in my house, and was sometimes instructed by Alfie as a student would be. "You are not learning your numbers. You have to repeat them over and over." Or Alfie would make him perform unpleasant tasks. "Roquefort, look at all the dirt you tracked in. The committee says you have to lick every bit of it up with your tongue or get a beating."

I continually took Roquefort's part, expressing anger and disappointment that he was treated so poorly. "That rules committee is certainly a mean bunch of vampires," I said repeatedly.

In the weeks that followed, Alfie developed a bemused tolerance for Roquefort and occasionally interceded with the rules committee on his behalf. There were echoes of my own defense of Roquefort in Alfie's tolerant attitude toward this imaginary young companion. Roquefort was even allowed to enjoy himself a little at times, and to shirk his duties without Alfie reporting him to the committee. I began to think that Alfie was enjoying Roquefort's misbehavior and said so to Alfie. He disagreed, but without much conviction.

At the same time as Alfie became more tolerant of Roquefort, I became more than tolerant of Linda, accepting her weekend gifts of food, which she had continued even after I almost ran over her. On a cold October day, right after I got the news that Alfie's grandmother, Gwen, had passed away and his grandfather had gone into an assisted living home, I asked Linda to join me for coffee.

We were just finishing our second cup after concluding that something very bad must have happened to Alfie's mother and that, with no other relative to take him, I might have to raise the boy. The thought was overwhelming, but Linda pointed out how lucky Alfie was to have me. And, she added, "For you to have him."

Alfie spent a few days in tearful remembrance of his grandmother Beth and asked repeatedly for his mother. Then one day, in the midst of a tearful deluge he asked me, "Who's going to take care of me?"

"Why, I am, Alfie."

"But you're so old," he wailed. "And you don't like vampires."

My face burned with shame, and I felt so bad for my little vampire I wanted to cry too. A great wave of sadness washed over me, followed by a backwash that left only a great feeling of love for this little boy. I held out my hand to him and he came to me, threw his arms about my waist, and held tight for several minutes before letting go. After a big hug from me, he withdrew to his room, and I asked Linda to come over: I needed someone to share what had happened and she was really the only one I could think of. None of my buddies at work would do. We sat quietly drinking coffee after I'd told her what had happened, no further words being necessary. Our quiet companionship was interrupted by a door banging open.

Alfie came barging into the kitchen, causing Linda to gasp and me to jerk around. In his hand was the bag of marbles that had, since his arrival, lain untouched in the toy box Beth had once put together for him. His chin jutted out and his green eyes shone with something akin to joy. Without a word, he twisted the fishnet marble bag and let it untwist. Centrifugal force whirled the marbles to the edges of the transparent bag creating a large, multicolored, swirling marble donut. It was found art.

"Why Alfie," Linda said, "that's beautiful."

"And I know how to play bowling with them too," Alfie said.

I was too dumbstruck to respond, but Linda looked at me and said, "Well, Jack, why don't you bowl a line with him?" She stood and walked to the door. "I'll leave you two for now. Have fun."

Though a little awkward, I kneeled down on the floor and took one of the large marbles he handed me. For pins he set up some wooden blocks I'd earlier given him. He selected another of the marbles and told me I could go first.

After he had with obvious pleasure beaten me at bowling I observed. "Vampires aren't supposed to play. Or enjoy it so much if they do. Won't the committee punish you for this behavior."

Alfie's face broke out into the widest smile I'd ever seen. "I'm president of the vampires' rules committee now. I make all the rules."

THE MAN WITH A KNIFE

With the knife pointed at her stomach, terror constricted Barbara's chest. Her mouth went dry and when she tried to say something, no words came.

"Get your ass inside. Now!" The man pushed her backward into the ground floor apartment. With his free hand, he pulled the hood of his black jacket forward, obscuring all but his black eyes, flared nostrils, and tense mouth.

She was frozen, unable to move so he grabbed her by the arm and pushed her back.

"Don't do anything silly," he hissed, and let her go.

She backed farther away as he advanced on her, not knowing if she should grab something to hit him with or keep her hands at her sides. "Wh . . . Wha . . . What do you want?"

"Anybody here but us?"

She couldn't speak. Her four-and-a-half-year-old was in day school, but her other three babies, three, one-and-a-half and one-month-old, were inside, all down for an afternoon nap. She couldn't let this man know! God help her, she couldn't let him know.

"Lady! Pay attention. I don't want to hurt you, but you better answer me."

"No, just me."

He stepped closer to her. She smelled rancid alcohol on his breath.

"Where do you keep your cash?" he asked, never taking his eyes off her. Worn cuffs belonging to a paisley shirt stuck out the ends of the worn jacket sleeve as he extended the knife toward her face.

"It's in the sewing room. In my purse." She turned and walked away from him, her shoulders squared and her backbone full of the iron her German father had bequeathed her. She called on the serenity of her English mother to help her not scream.

As he followed, the heels of his boots clicked on the hardwood floors, filling the entryway with enough noise to waken her girls. She wanted to shout at him, "Can't you walk a little more lightly?" But she was afraid. By the time they made it from the entryway to the door of the sewing room without a sound coming from the bedroom where the girls slept, her knees were weak and one leg trembled so hard she had to lean into the door jamb to keep from falling.

"Go on now. I ain't got all day."

She willed herself forward to a small table where her purse lay alongside a doll and some coloring books. When she picked it up and reached in to get her money, he held out his hand. She was terrified he would notice the toys and ask about the children.

"Give it to me."

"Please don't take my purse. It's got my driver's license and half my make-up in it. Let me just give you the money." She'd been to Macy's only the day before and spent over ten dollars on lip gloss and skin cream. "I'll get the money out."

He pursed his lips in disgust. "Then just do it," he grumbled.

She rummaged around until she came up with her wallet and took out the two hundred and seventy-five dollars her husband had given her for the week's expenses. Her hand trembled as she held it out to him.

"What about change?"

She closed her eyes, took a deep breath and fished out her coin purse. There were several nickels, dimes, and pennies and a couple of quarters inside and she dumped them into her palm and laid them on the table. "There. Satisfied?"

"This all you got in this house?"

She tried to look sincere. "I think that's all."

"Think harder."

"There's some small bills in a cookie jar in the kitchen."

He waved the knife again, herding her toward the connecting door. She almost slipped and fell on one of Betty's pull toys, but he grabbed her elbow and steadied her.

"You got a kid here?"

"No. They're at their grandmother's."

"You sure?"

Before she could answer, the front doorbell chimed. The musical notes jangled her nerves. Now she really wanted to scream.

"Who the fuck is that?"

Oh, God, she thought. I invited Gretchen over for coffee at three. Barbara had just plugged the percolator in when the buzzer had gone off five minutes ago, leaving it perc while she went to open the door, believing it to be Gretchen. Instead, she was greeted by the knife in the hand of this large, brown-skinned man dressed in blue jeans and a hood pulled over his head so that he appeared to be peering from under a shroud. "It's my friend coming for coffee."

The buzzer sounded again, longer this time.

"Don't answer it."

"I'm not that silly." She prayed, though, that Gretchen would sense something wrong and call the police.

The chiming stopped and the outside door clicked open and closed again, banging shut. How had she gotten into the foyer? Who let her in? Who let this man in? Which one living in the other six units on that wing had let them in? Was it one of the couples on third that belonged to that fringe religious group? The neighbor with the two boys whose car they'd borrowed to drive to the hospital? That single young man who played the guitar at all hours of the night and day? Or maybe the crotchety old couple. One of the Korean couple? She'd find out and let them have it. Sweat broke out on the man's face as Gretchen knocked on her door. Then banged on it. Please just go away she thought.

A moment later, when she heard the outside door open and close again, she breathed out in relief.

"Mommy?"

Horrified she whirled around to see Mary standing in the doorway of the playroom. The man held the knife at his side. She broke into a cold sweat, but went to the child, knelt down, put her arms around the small shoulders and spoke, much too sharp. "What's the matter?"

"I heard something."

"It was just someone knocking."

She peered around her mother at the man. "Who's he?"

"Just a friend of your daddy's. He came over to get something. You get back in bed now."

Tears sprang to the child's eyes and a pout started to form on her pretty face.

"You mind your momma, you hear?" The man spoke in a kind, firm voice that carried weight with Mary, who turned and walked quietly back to bed.

THE MAN WITH A KNIFE

"Thank you," Barbara whispered.

"You're welcome." A tremor at the corner of his mouth, she thought, could have been a smile. "You got a sweet kid. Got a great three-year-old myself." The man frowned, "Now let's get on here."

As they entered the kitchen, the rich smell of the Folgers coffee filled her nostrils, helping calm her. She opened the cookie tin and took out the packages of Oreos and Fig Newtons, then dumped the nearly five dollars in quarters into her hands and laid them gently on the table. He scooped them into his free hand and deposited them in his left coat pocket.

The phone shrilled and they jumped as if they'd been poked with sticks.

"Shiiit," he said, rolling the *i*'s as if he were caressing them, and pointed the knife at her again. "Don't you answer that."

"It's probably just my friend calling to see why I didn't answer the door." She hoped it wasn't her husband. He worked right across the street and could be home in two minutes if she didn't answer and it spooked him. She prayed it wasn't him. He would come home into the middle of this and God knows what this man might do to him. She began to breathe fast and felt lightheaded. "Slow down your breathing," she told herself. "I can't hyperventilate and pass out."

The phone shrilled again and both flinched.

"Do you have to keep that knife pointed at me?"

He lowered the knife till it was pointing more at her feet than her chest. "Don't you go trying anything, now."

"I'm not stupid. You've got my money. Now will you go?" Her breathing slowed and she let out a deep sigh.

"You mind I have a cup of that coffee? I almost froze waitin' outside 'fore I came in."

She caught herself before she laughed. He had a knife on her and had taken all her money. Now he was asking permission for a cup of coffee? "Sure," she said. Going into the cabinet she took out an insulated tin cup, one of four she'd taken a fancy to while she was in the hospital with Jeanie, and filled it. "You take cream and sugar?"

"Just sugar, please." He pushed the hood of his jacket back off his head revealing premature balding. There was a small keloid scar above his right eyebrow. His mouth was relaxed now, and he looked less threatening.

"That's the way my husband takes it," she said.

"Never did like cream in my coffee. Makes it taste like flavored milk." He laid the knife on the counter next to him and took a sip.

"That's just a paring knife," Barbara said. Terrified until now, she really hadn't looked all that close. In his hand the blade looked large and horrifying, but lying there on the counter, it appeared more appropriate for peeling potatoes than used as a weapon.

He shrugged. "It's sharp." He finished the hot coffee in quick gulps, some dribbling down his chin. Reaching up with the back of his hand, he swiped it away, then picked up the knife. "Thanks. We got to go now."

"We? We've got to go? I can't leave my baby."

He stood silently for a moment. "I just can't let you stand here by that telephone and call the police soon's I'm out the back door. You got to come."

"What if she wakes up again?" She felt panicked. She'd become calm, but now her heart began racing again, and she felt a pounding in her temples.

"Don't you worry none. We just going to walk down to the end of the alley and then you can come back. Take no more'n three or four minutes."

The panic faded, her heart slowed, and she wanted now only to get him out of the apartment as soon as she could. She started for the back door.

"You wait, now. Let me have a look." He parted the white curtains she'd spent two hours making when they first moved in, and looked carefully for a minute, his back to her. She looked at a butcher knife lying on the cabinet, and had the brief thought that she could grab it and put it in his back before he knew what was happening.

As if sensing her thoughts, he turned and looked at her, his eyes narrowed. "We going to walk out there like we was going on an errand or something. Don't you do anything like screaming or telling anybody anything."

"It's cold out there. All I've got on is this blouse. I'll freeze."

"Well, don't you got a jacket or something?"

"In the front closet."

"We got to go back where that baby can hear us again?"

"We can be quiet."

"You be a lot of trouble, lady," he said, but tip-toed back with her to the closet. The sight of this overgrown mugger tip-toeing in his construction boots again almost caused Barbara to laugh. They passed the open door of the bedroom as they approached the closet where she took her blue down jacket from its hanger. He nodded in the direction of the open door and whispered. "You be hidin' anything under your mattress? In that bedside table?"

"No. I mean, I don't think so," she stammered. Another wave of panic forced her to step back from him. "No! Absolutely not. There's no money in there."

"Let's go see."

She stood stock still. "I'm not lying."

He took her by the arm, the second time he'd touched her and his grip was strong, though he did not squeeze enough to hurt her. "We goin' in there anyway."

She froze and he put the knife at her ribs again. Her bladder began to cramp and she was afraid she would lose control.

"Don't be that way," he hissed. "You goin' to wake the baby."

She let him push her into the room, then, where he lifted first one corner of the bed then the other while he kept the knife pointed at her. Up against the wall at the head of the bed, she stood trembling while he rifled the drawers and found nothing but the book she was reading, a half-eaten Mars bar, batteries for her pen light, a vaginal lubricant, a package of Kleenex, and at the bottom, half a dozen or more pennies. "Holdin' out on me," he said, a note of humor creeping into his voice.

"I forgot about the damn pennies," she hissed.

He picked up the lubricant and as if he'd just noticed, he gazed at her breasts.

Barbara's mother had once told about Cynthia, a seventy-year-old neighbor, who had been in the bathroom taking a bath. Finished, she had wrapped a towel around herself and stepped into the bedroom. A man stood there with a gun pointing at her. "Get your hands up!" he'd said. She let go the towel and lifted both hands. The man had taken one wild look at her in all her glory, had screamed, "Oh my God," and fled. Barbara was terrified this man would not be so shy. Her cramping bladder threatened to explode.

But he shook his head as if clearing it of something. "What am I thinking about? My wife'd smell another woman on me a block away. She'd take this knife and carve my liver out." He shook his head, "I be thinkin' what a damn fool I be for taking so much time with you. I oughta be a mile away by now."

She took a deep breath and let it out slowly.

"Let's get outta here before you think of something else to busy me with." He stuck the knife into his pocket and leaving the pennies where they were, motioned with his head that she should go before him.

As they walked quietly toward the back of the house, she was sure that she could not make it to the bathroom off the kitchen that her husband used for a study. "I've got to go potty," she announced and ducked through the door and into the toilet.

"Lord Jesus," he yelped and hurried after her, sticking his foot in the door before she could close it. "I swear I should knock you in the head and be done with it."

"Can't you please shut the door?"

"And lock yourself in there? You'd be a fool to think I'd do that."

"Do you think I'd lock this door and leave you alone with my baby, you're the fool."

When she emerged, he was holding her husband's laptop computer. "I guess I'll be taking this, too."

"Won't do you any good. The thing doesn't work anymore. The motherboard burned out." She hoped he didn't notice the color rising into her face at the lie.

"Well damn," he said, and laid it back on the desk. "Ain't a whole lot else in here but books and papers. Any money?"

"No, just his books and papers." This wasn't a lie.

Taking her back into the kitchen, he went to the window and surveyed the backyard and alley. Satisfied, he opened the door and let her through. Outside, the knife now in his pocket, he walked down the steps beside her, out past the garbage cans and into the alley. Guided her south, past the parking lot beside the La Fiesta and on past the slum building that sat next door. A large black woman peered over the balcony at them and he waved to her. She waved back then disappeared inside.

He stopped, took out a package of cigarettes and lit one. "You want one?"

"Yes," she said, and took one from the pack. He lit it for her from his still-burning match.

She took a deep drag and let it out in an explosion of smoke. She began to feel calmer. "This is not a good way to make a living. You know what's going to happen if you get caught?" she said.

"It ain't how I normally make a living. I lost my job." His eyes grew moist and he wiped at them. "I've got two babies to feed." He motioned for her to start walking, his face grown hard again.

"And how do you think I'm going to feed my four? You just took my week's grocery money, you know."

"I thought you had one baby."

"Well, I lied. I'm sorry." She wanted to kick herself for that slip of the tongue.

"How come you said one?"

"I was afraid. I didn't want to tell you."

"Fuck, lady, I wouldn't hurt kids. Really wouldn't hurt you, unless I had to."

They reached the end of the alley as it opened on to 62nd Street. He looked both ways. There was no one on the street. Reaching into his pocket, he peeled away half the money he had taken and thrust it into her hand.

Then he turned and ran.

SUGARFOOT

The rope pulled tight around Sugarfoot's girth and to my surprise, the horse sat down. In all of my five-and-a-half years, I'd never seen a horse sit and was sure doing so was even more a surprise for him. Even more astonishing, Pa, that's what I called my grandfather Wilkerson, grabbed the horse's head and twisted until he fell over onto his side. His hooves scrabbled at the ground, sending up a spray of fine dust until Pa's helper slipped a rope over his two back legs and tied them together, then did the same to his front legs, and then pulled all four tight together. Sugarfoot lay helpless.

My heart trip-hammered. I was scared by what was happening to Sugarfoot. And couldn't understand why they were doing it. There was a lot I didn't understand about farm life when we came to visit when I was five and though we'd lived with Granny and Pa before, I'd been too young to observe things like what was happening to Sugarfoot. I was more of a town boy than a country boy.

My daddy, mamma, sister, and I had been living in Wichita Falls, Texas, for several months before early September of 1938 when daddy decided to travel the three hundred miles to the Wilkerson homeplace in Northeast Oklahoma. Soon after arriving, he left my mamma, sister, and me and went back to Texas with the stated purpose of finding a job. He'd hawked Jewel Tea products for almost a year, a long time for him to stay on one job before quitting in a fuming rage. He said there was a good chance of finding something in Fort Worth or Waco, Texas, and when he did, he promised to come get us. Days went by, then weeks with no good word from him. Jobs were scarce, my granny said.

During those weeks, I learned to love the three horses Pa owned. There was Trixie, the mare, who was edgy and a little ill-tempered, though she never gave me the mean eye usually reserved for strangers. I fed her clumps of fresh grass pulled from the yard and she lipped them into her mouth without ever taking my hand with them. She bore a colt every year or two and at the time Sugarfoot lay trussed in the barnyard she was several months into a new pregnancy. Sugarfoot was a yearling and still tried to nurse at times, though he was as large as she. And though pregnant, Pa still led her into the field and hitched her and Tony, his other workhorse, to the two-bottom plow they pulled through the rocky soil.

Old Tony was a bay gelding so tall that by stooping a little, I could have walked under his belly, though I never did. I feared he might step on me. I did enjoy riding him from the horse-lot to the field where Pa worked him and Trixie. Pa would lift me high onto his back, and I would come to rest just behind Tony's withers, then grab and hang tight to the horse collar. From there, I looked down on all the adults who usually towered over me. And in my childish way I fantasized that Old Tony's muscles, power, and strength were my own and his will subservient to me. Though Pa never let go the reins, I called out, "giddy-up, gee and haw, and whoa" and Pa, in good-natured compliance, would walk the horse forward, turn him left or right, or bring him to a halt.

Most of all I loved Sugarfoot, a tall, gangly bay with a white star on his forehead and white stockings. When I first saw him, I asked Pa if he would give the animal to me. Pa was sitting in an oak rocker out under the walnut trees whittling on a piece of kindling, and occasionally spitting snuff into a coffee can. "Well now, Clifton," he said, "You'd have no place to keep him once your daddy fetches you."

"We nearly always have a backyard with lots of grass," I assured him.

He waved his knife in a sweeping gesture that took in all the pasture and creek bottom where the horses ran, then said, "I'm sure he would feel cooped up and unhappy without all this space to run. You wouldn't want that, would you?"

I saw the reasonableness of that, but must have looked quite disappointed because Pa laid down his knife and took me on his knee. "I tell you what; as long as you're on the farm you can claim Sugerfoot as your own."

I couldn't be sure just how long that would be. My daddy was a restless man who found the rigors of work and home life too much for him to bear at times. We never stayed in one place more than a few months. We had moved from Hobart, where I was born, to Gotebo, then Rocky, and on to Altus before leaving Oklahoma for Texas. First there was Vernon then Wichita Falls. My sister had attended six or seven different schools in the six years since her first grade. Periodically, my daddy would deposit us at one of my grandparents' farms and take off; where he'd go and when he'd come back were always matters of conjecture. So, I might own Sugarfoot for a day or two, a week or a month, or even longer. But I'd been free to call

Sugarfoot my own for three weeks before my Pa and the vet threw him to the ground and hogtied him.

It was in early October that I saw Sugarfoot taken down in the barn lot. Earlier that morning as Pa and I walked outside on our way to do chores, we saw the first frost of autumn covering the grass and weeds. "That will have killed off the rest of those damn flies. It'll be a good day to attend to Sugarfoot," he said.

The flies were a nuisance; the whole time I'd been living on the farm they'd buzzed in and around the house, all over the yard, the horse-lot, and in my ears. Now that the full warmth of the sun was gone, so were they. I was glad there would be no flies that day but had no idea what that had to do with Sugarfoot.

"You want to help?" Pa asked as he turned the setting hens out into the yard.

"Yes," I said. We walked on to the barn where he set me to shucking feed corn and scrubbing the kernels loose on a washboard while he milked the jersey cow, Clara.

We took the corn to the pigs that grunted and squealed in anticipation as we approached. Pa said, "You're sure now, you want to help? You've not been too keen to help out since we took Clara over to the Clemen's bull. Remember?"

How could I forget? One morning Pa had said, "I've got to get Clara bred. You want to come along?"

I was thrilled to go along. Since I'd arrived, he'd taken me with him to pick up and haul rocks out of the plowed ground, I'd helped bring winter firewood in from the hollow, and I'd ridden along into Siloam Springs, Arkansas, to help load chicken feed and oyster shells to haul back to the farm in the trunk of the car. I'd even watched as he forced a neighbor's horse to drink a quart bottle of medicine to cure his colic, handing him the bottle and taking it back when he was done. So, when he asked if I wanted to help take Clara over to get bred, I was all for it.

"Why do you have to take Clara to get bread?" I asked, wondering why he had to go to the Clemen's for bread when granny baked bread every day. Or, why he would need to take Clara.

"So, she can have a calf."

That made no sense to me. "How does that happen?"

Pa just laughed and said, "You'll see."

I had seen, too, more than I really wanted to see but when Pa put Clara in with the bull, I had to leave the shed, sure the huge animal was going to kill Clara whom I had grown fond of because of the enormous amounts of milk she gave. I was quite relieved ten minutes later when Pa led Clara out of the barn and she looked none the worse for being "bread." But I now thought that bread could be something good to eat or something quite frightening. It was not till years later after I learned to read and write, that I knew the difference between B-R-E-D and B-R-E-A-D.

Now, standing with my Pa and remembering Clara, I asked, "You're not going to take Sugarfoot to get bread, are you?"

"No." Pa laughed.

"Oh," I said, relieved that Pa would not let the bull treat Sugarfoot the way he had Clara. "Does Sugarfoot have the colic?" I asked remembering the time I helped dose the neighbor's sick horse.

"No, he's just fine. "We're just going to fix it so's he can't produce any colts." Before he could explain further, Granny called us to breakfast and I took off for the kitchen; my Granny's food trumped hearing Pa's explanation.

When I'd first arrived three weeks earlier, Granny had swept me up into her arms and almost smothered me in her ample bosom. She smelled of talcum powder and the sweat she'd raised tending her vegetable garden. She'd been digging up the last of her summer potatoes when our car pulled in. A heavy woman with a wide snaggle-tooth smile, she had only five teeth still left in her mouth, and her skin was soft as the feather mattress she laid out for me at bedtime. Pa, Granny, Uncle Keith, and Aunt Charlene lived in the farmhouse that had only two rooms: one, a kitchen that held a huge cook-stove, a cream separator, oak dining table with unmatched chairs, and a closet filled with clothes, shoes, and a wooden egg crate; and the other, a sleeping room furnished with two double beds, a bureau, dresser, oak rocking chair, and a cast iron, wood-burning stove. At bedtime, I was favored with a child-sized down mattress laid on a folding cot and Uncle Keith slept on a pallet made up with two folded quilts laid out on the kitchen floor. The other six shared the double beds. At five and a half years of age I did not feel this arrangement crowded. My father, however, found it unbearable, and lit out for Waco and parts south after the first night.

On the morning I saw Sugarfoot sit down, my pencil thin thirteen-year-old sister, Geraldine, and heavyset aunt, Charlene (known by all as Skinny Winnie and Fatty Arbuckle) wolfed down their breakfast, and then scooted out the door headed for the school bus stop a half-mile away. They were "thick as thieves," as my mamma said, and when not in school, disappeared into the woods and hollows nearby. I sometimes made their disappearing acts difficult as I sneaked along behind to spy on them. On a previous visit during the hot summer, I caught them skinny dipping in the pool near the old Indian tanning grounds, and they'd tried to keep me quiet about it by including me in their raid on Pa's watermelons. All would have gone well had I not inadvertently spilled watermelon juice down my front and left a couple of seeds to dry on my pants. We all suffered a scolding for that, me more so for trying to lie about my involvement even as my mother and Pa stared at the incriminating evidence plastered to my pants.

My Uncle Keith, who was sixteen and also had to be off to catch the school bus, had to bring up the horses from the draw before he followed the two girls, leaving the rest of us at breakfast.

As Pa finished his coffee, he mentioned to Granny and Mamma that I was going to help him with Sugarfoot.

My mamma's face screwed up into a worried frown. "Don't you think Clifton a little young to be seeing what you and that vet's doing?"

"Boy's got to learn hard things sometime. The sooner the better, I say."

Finished with my bacon, biscuits and gravy, I left the kitchen before my mother could summon enough courage to backtalk Pa. Keith had just driven the horses into the barnyard when I reached the gate. His chore finished, he ran for the house to grab his lunch and trot down the road to the corner where he, too, would catch the school bus.

The horses hadn't been worked for a few days and were a little skittish, so I stayed behind the barbed wire gate and watched as they ran back and forth along the barnyard fence. The barn was a solid, two-story structure made out of old roughhewn boards that had never seen a coat of paint and had weathered to a glossy gray color that turned black when wet from the rain. Since the harvest that fall, its loft was stacked full of corn and hay used to feed the animals. I was not fond of the barn; it seemed dark and forbidding to me and was infested with rats, mice, and chickens which flew into the hayloft to lay their eggs and would peck at me if I came too close. I stayed outside the fence and watched Tony and Trixie as they settled down, though Sugarfoot kept raising his head and tail and trotting back and forth between the gate to the pasture and the fence where I stood. I held out some grass to him, but he was too agitated to take it.

Old Tony trotted over and snuffed at the grass I held out to him and then lipped it out of my hand. The smartest of the three horses that roamed Pa's farm, he'd learned on his own to drop the simple gate that led into the yard and on into the open road. With a hoof on the bottom loop of wire that held the gatepost, he would slip the top wire loose, causing the gate to fall open. Uncle Keith received two scoldings before Pa realized that it wasn't a forgetful son who didn't close the gate, but a wise old horse that opened it. As I scratched Old Tony's nose, we heard a car turning into the drive. Old Tony shied away and I turned to see a shiny, black '38 Ford drive into the yard and park.

Pa joined the driver, and the two of them strolled toward me, the stranger carrying a large black bag. As they came near Pa said, "Dr. Miller, this is Clifton, my grandson. He's going to help us today."

Dr. Miller nodded to me and joined Pa, who had cut a piece of apple with the knife he generally used to cut a chaw from his chewing tobacco, and held it out to the horses. That brought the horses over and when Sugarfoot came close, Pa tried to slip a noose around his head, but he shied away.

Opening the gate, Pa and the vet separated Sugarfoot from the other two horses and drove them out of the barnyard. Sugarfoot circled the barnyard at a run, calling to Trixie who answered with a nervous whinny. He charged at the gate, but pulled up just as it seemed he would crash into the barbed wire. The men then drove him into a corner where the vet threw a rope over his neck, and then Pa slipped two more looped ropes over the horse's neck and then over his front legs and down to his flank and loins. Pa stood on one side, the vet on the other, and they pulled the ropes taught.

That was when Sugarfoot sat down and Pa bulldogged him. He held tight to the horse's head while the vet tied the horse's four legs together.

Sugarfoot gave a high-pitched scream that trailed off into a whinny. A few days earlier I'd heard a stallion scream that way when Pa and I had ridden Trixie past. He had screamed and butted his chest up against his wooden corral, and I was sure he would break out. I was as scared now as I was then.

"Hey Clifton, bring Dr. Miller's bag over here," Pa yelled.

Dragging my feet, I took the bag to him, though I did not want to get near. Sugarfoot's head was twisted so far backward I thought it would break and his eyes were wide in terror. I wanted to cry.

"Give it to Dr. Miller there."

A few days earlier I'd helped my Granny by sewing a square for her quilt. I'd labored for the better part of two hours hand-stitching the eight pieces she'd cut and laid out for me. Despite the numerous puncture wounds to my fingers, I'd managed to cobble together a square which my Granny praised and hugged me for, but I could see that my large looping stitching didn't compare to the neat ones my Granny made. I'd enjoyed hearing her stories about me as a baby. There was one I liked best. While the rest of the family was out picking wild plums to make jelly, my Granny had stayed behind with me. "All went well," she said, "until a sudden windstorm came up and began to shake the house to its very foundation." She stopped her sewing and her eyes widened as she continued, "I thought for sure the house was going to get blown away. I pulled up a loose floorboard, grabbed you up, stuffed you screaming like a banshee down between the studs, and lay down on top of you." She gave her widest snaggle-tooth grin and chucked me under the chin. "The house and I could have blown away and I wouldn't have cared. Not if my sweet baby was safe." Now I wanted to be with my Granny sewing quilt squares, digging the last of the potatoes, or helping wash the scores of metal pieces from the cream separator that needed cleaning every morning. Instead, I handed the black bag to Dr. Miller, backed up a few feet and stood watching.

Dr. Miller opened the bag, took out a long-bladed knife and some rubbing alcohol and walked behind Sugarfoot. He took hold of the bag that hung between Sugarfoot's back legs and sponged it off with the alcohol. To distract the horse, Pa bit down on Sugarfoot's ear as, with a quick stroke of the knife, Dr. Miller laid the bag open, then severed something from the bag and pitched it into the dirt of the cow lot. Sugarfoot gave an ear-splitting scream, then another, and another. I thought they would never stop. Dr. Miller poured more alcohol over the wound, capped the bottle and put it back into his bag. He grabbed some weeds from the fence row and wiped the blood from his knife and hands.

I glanced from Sugarfoot to the bloody mess that lay on the ground nearby, unable to imagine why they had done that to my horse. I was frightened, and hated that I had helped bring such pain to Sugarfoot. I watched, frozen to the spot, as Dr. Miller pulled the ropes loose from Sugarfoot's legs and Pa let go the head. The animal came to his feet, screaming as the ropes fell from around his middle. Struggling to his feet, he began galloping around and around the corral, giving forth shrill whinnies of agony, and kicking his back legs out as if to rid himself of the pain.

Pa turned to me and said, "Thanks for your help, Clifton." He and Dr. Miller then walked back toward the house leaving me momentarily standing by the gate, not knowing what to do.

I had wanted to be Pa's helper but now all I wanted to do was run to my mamma and Granny and sit in their laps while they rocked me.

Instead, I ran to the kitchen where Dr. Miller and Pa had finished washing their hands and sat down to the kitchen table. I stood in the door watching as they asked Granny for black coffee, which she poured into big-handled mugs. Too ashamed in front of the men to run close to Granny or walk past them to my mamma who was lost in her crocheting in the next room, I slipped into a chair across from my Pa.

I couldn't understand why my Granny and the men laughed when I asked for a cup of coffee.

GASSING UP

Serra Ramana looked out a window of the ARCO service station and made a face as she turned to Joanie, her coworker. "Would you stay another few minutes before you take off?" she implored. "That guy, Lamont, just drove in."

"That means trouble."

The young man driving the sports car had coffee-and-cream skin that matched the color of the car. He slowed and waved to them, but Serra looked away, pretending she had not seen, and observed another regular customer, an old Latino man named Ricardo, pull his Toyota Camry forward, unwittingly cutting Lamont off from the gas pump he was aiming for. Now she was sure there would be trouble.

She heard Lamont scream, "Hey, that's my pump, asshole," and saw him strike the dashboard with his fist. But the old man continued forward at a snail's pace, his black Toyota inching perilously close to the glossy, slick side of Lamont's 2005 Saturn SC2. His tires screeching, Lamont wheeled around to the other side of the pumps.

"You're in luck, Serra. Lamont's not his worst self today. He didn't get out and tear that guy's head off," Joanie said.

But Lamont gunned his motor, and both young women watched as he jerked open his door and confronted the old man.

"You shouldn't have done that. That was wrong."

Serra recognized the tone as the one Lamont had used when he picked a fistfight with some redneck tow truck driver the previous Saturday night, so she reached for the phone to call 911, but Joanie took her arm.

"You call the police and Lamont might take it out on us. Wait."

They listened and watched as Ricardo looked up at Lamont and gave a calm smile. "I was waiting here before you. It was my turn at the pumps." He pulled a pair of brown gloves out of his jeans pocket and donned them.

"Bullshit. This ain't right. You ought to be ashamed for what you did. Where's your manners?"

"Lamont expecting good manners from somebody is just too much," Serra whispered softly, afraid Lamont might hear her if she spoke any louder.

The target of Lamont's moral outrage only shrugged his shoulders as if to say, "No shame here," unhooked the gas hose from the pump, and stuck it in his tank.

"What the fuck you shruggin' yor shoulders for, motha-fucka. I be talkin' to you about your bad manners." Lamont took off his Bulls baseball hat, smoothed his hair back and placed the hat firmly back on his head, most assuredly readying himself for a fight.

Ricardo reached out, flipped the pump lever up and started pumping gas as if he wasn't hearing a word Lamont said. He unbuttoned the white sports shirt he wore outside his pants to let in the faint breeze that struggled to temper the July heat.

GASSING UP

"Now a fight will start," Serra predicted, but Lamont jumped back in his car, drove around to the other pump rolled out the car, and headed for the door. Serra blanched when he came in. Her dark skin would not protect her from Lamont's scorn, he'd let it be known he despised Asians as much as whites, Latinos, and Mexicans.

"I'm gonna teach that old man a lesson, Serra." He pounded his fist on the counter, "And you don't go callin' the police like last time." He stormed out again.

"Shouldn't you go ahead and call the police?" Joanie asked Serra, her hand trembling as she laid it on the receiver.

"Listen, Joanie, the last time he caused trouble and we called the police, Lamont threatened to enter an unmentionable part of our bodies and do unspeakable things to us."

The young cashier nodded, looking miserable and afraid. "And I think he's capable of doing it, too."

"Then we shouldn't get involved." Both girls jumped when they heard Lamont's voice raised again.

"I hates you, you Mexican motha-fucka. I hates all motha-fuckin' Mexicans and whites." Lamont bellowed out, screamed out, challenging all the non-African Americans in the world who at that moment could hear him, though there was only one nearby, a white woman at the furthest pumps who retreated into the station's bathroom.

Lamont swung the nozzle of his pump hose around like it was a WWII flamethrower shown on late night cable TV, but Ricardo ignored him as he reached up and scratched his nose. Serra was amazed that Lamont's threats were as insignificant to Ricardo as an itch that had to be rubbed away.

Serra had noticed a young woman sitting with her baby for the last half hour in the service station's driveway at a shady spot under the elm trees of the house next door. During this latest spell of hot weather, she had sat there almost every day, gossiping quietly on the phone. She'd never caused any trouble. Serra gasped and Joanie put a hand to her mouth in shock, when the woman suddenly shouted, "You tell him, Lamont, all them Mexicans are a big pain in the ass."

"You hear the lady, man. She say you one big pain in the ass. She hate your Mexican ass too." Lamont was pacing back and forth on his side of the island, his streetwalking gait swaying dangerously, going faster and faster as if to gather enough momentum to propel him to the other side.

"You've got an attitude problem, mister." The words of the old man were measured and calm, like a principal talking to some small child that had been sent to his office.

"Damn right I gots me an attitude. Around you motha-fuckin' spics I always gots me an attitude. But it ain't no problem for me, you motha-fucka. It's a problem for you and all the rest of you motha-fuckas." His voice seemed to reach the heights of falsetto with "motha," and then bottomed out with, "fuckas," using the whole range of the scale to vent his angry displeasure. The high notes made the intercom between the pumps and the cashier's cage screech.

"You're a bigot, mister." The old man looked up at Lamont for the first time and Serena could see no fear in his eyes.

"Man, what you say? I'm an accountant. I got me my BA at the University of Kentucky and I got me my MA from the University of Illinois and I got my MBA. I work for a bunch of white motha-fuckas right down there in the loop who I don't take no more shit off of than I will you." Lamont clenched and unclenched his fists. He reached up every little bit and gave the bill of his cap a touch, like he was a Cubs ballplayer using magic rituals to guarantee his luck at the plate.

"I'm glad to hear you're educated but I suppose that just makes you an educated bigot with an attitude."

"Hatin' your Mexican ass don't make me no bigot. Whuppin' your ass won't do it either." As if an invisible barrier had been lowered,

GASSING UP

Lamont stomped over into Ricardo's side of the island and towered over him, both hands balled into permanent fists, mouth working like he had something to say, but just couldn't get it out, his handsome face contorted so that his own mother wouldn't have recognized him.

Serra saw that the old man showed no fear or anger but just kept pumping gas, giving Lamont about as much attention as if the hate-filled young man was a gnat circling his head. She looked at Joanie who was shaking her head as if in disbelief.

Lamont stood toe to toe with Ricardo, his $150 loafers touching the tired rubber of the other's walking shoes. He glared down into the age-wrinkled face, but Ricardo just looked straight ahead, as if studying the patterns on his tormentor's T-shirt. "You ain't payin' no attention, old man. You don't think I can't whup you? Is that it, motha-fucka? You think you some kind of tough asshole?"

"Don't be ridiculous. Of course you can whip me." Ricardo looked up and smiled at Lamont like he was surprised that such a smart young man could be so dense.

But Lamont raised a fist to hammer a blow down on the old man's head. "What you say? You call me ridiculous?"

"No, I just think it would be ridiculous to fight you. There'd be no contest."

That stopped Lamont for a moment and he stood there, his fist raised, studying Ricardo pumping gas like he was some strange object too hard to figure out. He scratched at his crotch and shook his head but then his eyes lit up and he said "I sure do wish you was younger. I'd whup your ass then." He lowered his fist and it appeared to Serena that he had given up on the idea of actually pummeling the poor old fellow who smiled for the first time.

"Well I don't know, probably. But maybe not," the Ricardo said. "I was pretty tough when I was younger."

"What? You don't think I could whup yo ass if you was younger?"

"Well, I have to admit that if I was younger there's one thing I sure couldn't do and that's beat your mouth."

Serra's own mouth dropped. "Joanie, did you hear that?"

"Yea, and Lamont didn't hit the old man. He punched that other guy out for saying a lot less."

But by this point it seemed Lamont had completely given up on the violent approach and had decided to embark on another form of intimidation. He jumped up on the eighteen-inch cement bumper guard at the end of the pumps and towered over the old man. "I'm from Kentucky, motha-fucka, and I'm proud of my mouth. I can outtalk any motha-fucka down there and I can outtalk any Mexican up here."

"Why is it that I really believe that without question?" The old man raised his eyes to Lamont standing nearly eight feet tall, and Lamont grinned down as though he had scored a real point, getting some agreement for the first time. Emboldened by this victory he made another effort to humble the dwarf standing below him.

"Man, you is bald." He reached down and touched the balding pate below him and then moved his hand on down over his cheek. "And you needs a shave—bad. You is old and you is grungy."

"Look, you can bad mouth me all you want, threaten me all you want, but don't touch me disrespectfully. Didn't your mother ever teach you manners?"

"I don't take no shit from any man—I don't care who he is or how old he is. My boss, he your age. He give me shit, I beat him up and find me another job." Lamont beat his fist into his palm several times, as if savoring the thought of pounding that big meat grinder into his boss's face.

"I don't recommend that kind of behavior. You'll be going from one job to the next all your life. What kind of an existence is that?" Ricardo hung up the gas hose and walked toward his car door.

Lamont did something then that was totally incomprehensible to Serra. He jumped from his lofty perch and, with a sweeping bow, opened

Ricardo's car door for him. Whether it was a parting shot of some kind or a show of respect, only he could know.

"Thank you," the old man said, as he reached down and pushed the lock button, shut the door, and turned toward the station entrance.

Lamont looked dumbfounded for a moment and then, dropping the street talk, said, "You don't trust me? I'm really hurt."

"I'm sorry, but I'd have locked that door on any account. Things in unlocked cars have a way of disappearing, you know."

"But I wouldn't steal anything from you. I don't need to steal. Look at this." The wad of naked cash Lamont pulled from his pocket was thicker than most men's wallet.

"You better put that away or I'll be the one tempted to steal from you."

That was said deadpan and it looked to Serena like Lamont half believed it. He stuffed the wad of bills back in his pocket in a hurry.

"But what I'm saying is, I don't need anything of yours." He put his arm around the bony shoulders of the old man as they walked toward the door into the station. "And, locking your door? That was really insulting."

"No insult intended; I assure you."

"But it makes it look like you've got no trust. You've got to trust people; you hear what I'm saying?"

Ricardo stopped, put his arm up across Lamont's broad back, and rested his hand on a muscular shoulder. They were like father and son enjoying the closeness of each other. Ricardo went on to speak like a father to his inexperienced son, trying to help him understand about trust. "I'll admit I'm having an awful hard time understanding your idea of trust. What if some guy came up to you—he's four inches taller than you and outweighs you by forty or fifty pounds—and calls you a motha-fuckin' nigga—tells you he's going to whip your black ass. You're going to tell me you'd trust him?"

"Hell, no." Lamont's voice lowered, he reverted back to the street vernacular and bent forward as though imparting an important message to a trusted friend. Serena could barely hear him say, "I'd get my 357-magnum out of my glove compartment and blow that mother-fucka ahhhh-way."

"Now, look at you." Ricardo declared, sounding disappointed, "You've just been trying so hard to convince me I was wrong to mistrust you, and then, what do you do? You tell me you've got a gun you could shoot me with. How's that going to build trust? You're are a hard man to trust, you know that, don't you?"

Lamont didn't answer. He walked into the station with Ricardo and over to the window to pay for his gas, a look of puzzlement and not a little frustration clouding his face.

The woman who'd hidden in the bathroom earlier fled to her car.

The confrontation seemed to be over when Lamont walked to the door without another word. But then he turned. "What do you do, anyway?"

Ricardo smiled at him and gave an enigmatic shake of his head.

"Are you a policeman?" There was a trace of respect in Lamont's voice now.

Ricardo scolded, "Get outta here. Do I act like a cop?"

"Man, I don't know what you act like." Lamont turned and pushed through the door, his curiosity unsatisfied. He didn't give a backward glance as he drove sedately away, not bothering to lay down rubber.

Ricardo went to the window and handed Serena a twenty-dollar bill for his gas and a Hershey's candy bar.

"He's a regular jerk." Serra ventured.

"Yea, he was acting pretty awful," Ricardo agreed.

"Yes," she said. "And he comes here all the time." Her hands trembled as she handed back change to Ricardo like he was a guru and she a new devotee.

Joanie, her voice almost inaudible, asked. "Just how did you do what you just did with Lamont, sir, if I may ask?"

He seemed to consider that question for a moment and then his eyes twinkled, like he was going to let her in on a joke. "I learned a long time ago on the psych wards I worked on that you don't threaten men like that. They are too afraid. They are immature children in overgrown men's bodies." Then he shook his head. "And if you threaten them, they attack."

He smiled at Serena and, going to his car and unlocking it, climbed in and drove slowly away from the pumps, waving at Serena before he turned on to the street in the opposite direction to which Lamont had taken.

MEMORIES OF RUTH

The invitation said, "Come to the twenty-fifth high school reunion of the Okeene, Oklahoma, Class of '51."

I almost tossed it; I'd failed to nurture any ties to Okeene, Oklahoma. But there was one person, my favorite high school teacher, Ruth Addis, I really wanted to see and thoughts of her stayed my hand before I threw the invitation away. Then came a spark of curiosity about what had transpired in the lives of the other thirty-six Okeene High graduates of '51. Pen in hand, I filled out the registration form, wrote out a five-dollar check to cover the evening dinner, stuffed both into an envelope, and dropped it in the mail.

Four weeks later, on the way out of downtown Chicago, the O'Hare airport bus passed familiar places I'd come to know in the thirteen years since I'd left Oklahoma. The bus slowed as it neared the cultural center, and a traffic policeman, giving a "thumbs up" sign and a toothy smile, waved the driver through a yellow light. As we turned left on Ohio, passing Hanley Dawson Cadillac, we caught the lights in sequence, and were across the river bridge and on to the Kennedy freeway without a stop. Thirty minutes later, approaching the O'Hare airport turnoff, the horizon showcased five incoming planes and a helicopter, sky traffic thick as that of the morning rush hour creeping in on the inbound lanes. In Okeene, Oklahoma, there would be no traffic police, Cadillac dealer, or airport. I could drive across town in less than five minutes even if I had to stop at the one traffic light.

Sitting next to me, a tall African American woman, elegant as a model, dozed; her chin resting in her palm as the bus rocked her head up and down—back and forth, nodding in a perpetual affirmation or denial of whatever dreams may have been running through her hazy, early morning brain. In my hometown there would be no people of color on the streets. They were not welcome.

As we passed the Canfield Road exit, a plane slowly glided ahead of us and appeared to be landing on the very blacktop we traveled on. Settling its tractor-sized wheels to touch down on an O'Hare runway, it disappeared beneath a pale three-quarter moon that hung in the southwest sky, keeping company with a few scattered, early sunrise, crimson clouds.

Enormous billboards sporting inane cigarette and airline ads lined the road into the airport and reminded me of the lines, plagiarized from Joyce Kilmer, and mutilated by God knows whom:

*I think that I shall never see
a billboard lovely as a tree.
And if the billboards don't all fall,
I'll never see a tree at all.*

The bus wheezed to a halt and, carrying my suitcase, I passed through the crush of the terminal, boarded a 727 jet, and was on the way to a visit with the past. It was 1976, and I had lived in Chicago for thirteen years. Okeene now held nothing but memories to draw me there and I had not returned since attending the burial of my stepfather five years earlier. I had visited once before thirteen years earlier to attend my mother's funeral. Funerals and this reunion were all that had summoned me back to the place I'd spent the last three of high school.

It took only an hour and a half to reach Oklahoma City by air and then two hours to reach my "hometown," a three-and-a-half-hour journey that would pull me back twenty-five years.

In a rented Dodge Escort, I drove quickly through Oklahoma City and out into the country, where on either side of the narrow blacktop fields of wheat stubble stretched for miles. Giant, four-wheeled tractors pulled disc plows as clouds of red-brown dust trailed behind. Silver butane trailers, reflecting the brilliant midday sun, sat ready to service the machinery working the fields. Meadow larks flew up from the pasturelands and jackrabbits darted along the fence rows. Two pheasants dashed across the road, splashes of color in the otherwise dull, dusty black, green, and brown of the road, ditches, and fields. A hawk made a lazy circle and came to rest on a dead treetop that reached skyward.

As I approached the outskirts of Okeene, population 1,100, I saw the remains of a small billboard, the only one that had once welcomed visitors on this stretch of road. It was gone now, but the message it conveyed remained in my memory, "Only one life; will soon be past, only what's done for Christ will last." A quarter of a century before this little town had boasted thirteen churches. There were no fewer now, I supposed.

As I turned onto Main Street and slowed to a crawl, the 12:00 P.M. siren sounded, reaching into every house, piercing through the soft hum of air conditioners, the twanging conversations of housewives with their children, and the babble of canned commercials preceding the twelve-o'clock news. The air-raid quality of the blaring siren brought back images of Luftwaffe and Zeros to anyone forty years old or older. Those younger would only know that the siren marked three hours of the day: 12:00 noon, time for lunch; 6:00 P.M., time to close up and go home to dinner; 6:00 A.M., time to rise and meet the day.

As the last growl of the siren faded, bells from St. Mary's Catholic Church tolled, now dominating the airways, and even those souls at some distance from the far edges of town heard this reminder to the devout that this was the largest and most impressive church in town. Passing down the two blocks of Main Street businesses, I turned right on East E Street and rolled to a stop in front of the high school as the church bells faded to silence. Too early for the start of the reunion, I went inside the school thinking I'd look at the class pictures that I remembered lining the hallways. But now I found the walls empty. The pictures all dangled from a circular pole, and I could swing the years past with a flick of my fingers to see fifty years of bright-faced seniors looking out of that circling gallery. I turned to one that showed the thirty-six faces of those with whom I had graduated and the teachers who had shepherded us through those years.

I was surprised that there were faces of classmates I did not remember, though I recognized many others. That I had forgotten some made me uneasy. That and the fact that I could not imagine how those faces would look today, did not want to think of how aged my teachers would be, or how the lively, scrubbed faces of my classmates who had been little more than children would now be fading into middle age. I had looked in the mirror that morning at my own face. That was my best clue.

At the bottom of our picture was the class motto, "We have crossed the Bay, the Ocean lies ahead." My ship had taken me continents away from this place and that time. I had not seen nor heard from any of the people I'd meet at the reunion, all of them now strangers. It now pained me to be here, to feel like a stranger, and I wanted to return to my rented Dodge Escort, drive away, and never return.

I hurried from the building warring with myself, wanting to make an immediate full retreat. But first I'd visit my favorite teacher, Miss Ruth Addis, then make the decision. I had written her that I wanted to say hello and she had responded with a warm invitation to drop by. I could dismiss all those others, but not Ruth. So, I drove to the west edge of town where a row of newly built, one-story brick houses sat on what had once been prime wheatland. Each had an attached garage and recently planted lawn, now browned by summer heat. There were no cracks in the sidewalks or cement driveways, and they all had neat signs with the owners' names printed on them. It was hard to picture Ruth living in one of these cookie-cutter houses; for so many years she'd lived alone on her farm five miles out of town. Approaching her door, I walked past flower beds that sprouted only a few weeds and a scraggly moss rose or two and onto a front porch too small for a swing. When I'd visited Ruth's farm home more than twenty-five years ago, we'd gone out onto her long front veranda where she sat in an oak rocker while I pushed back and forth in a restful, creaking porch-swing. Here there was no veranda or even a porch large enough for an oak rocker nor a ceiling from which a swing could hang.

I rang the bell twice and there was no immediate answer, but before giving up and leaving, I heard movement, then the door swung wide. Ruth's eyes lighted in genuine pleasure when she recognized me. She stepped forward into my open arms and returned my bear hug, adding a strong pat on my back. Taking my arm, she ushered me into the living room and set me down in one of her yellow oak rockers. "Clifton, it's so good of you to come by." Her eyes twinkling, she reminded me, "I'm probably the only one in Okeene who ever called you Clifton and not Cliff."

"You're the only one that could get away with it, Ruth."

Ruth laughed out loud, a dryly humorous laugh that warmed me. Her reddish hair was now streaked with gray. Her slightly freckled face was older now but there was still the fiery blush beneath her cheeks and the laugh was still the same; neither had her love and respect for me, though it had been years since I'd seen her.

"But Clifton, I'll bet you haven't had any lunch yet and I want to fix something for you. I can only offer a ham sandwich and coffee but, if you want, I will do that." She rose, the osteoarthritic knots standing out on her knuckles as she grabbed the chair arms and pulled herself up.

"I'd rather spend time with you than eat," I said, truthfully, as I followed her into the kitchen. "So, anything you have is okay by me."

She set bread and meat on the table and poured me coffee. Then she cut a tomato in two, brought out cantaloupe and potato salad, and offered ice cream and angel food cake for dessert later.

"Your sandwich is like stone soup; you've added to it until it's a feast." I laughed. "I wonder what you would provide if you invited me to dinner."

"I really wish I had known what time you would be here so I could have prepared something nicer," she apologized sincerely, then sat down but did not serve herself. "I'm going to talk while you eat. I can eat later and I can't talk to you later, Clifton."

She folded her hands on the table and crossed her feet under the chair. "Clifton, I have had to come to terms with things lately. With the deaths in my family I have been faced with the fact of my mortality. I used to think I was immune from dying. It's like when I was a young woman, I thought I was pretty." She laughed her "the joke's on me" laugh, half rising from her chair as she did, then, settling back, covered her mouth with her fingers and looked away. Highlighted by the blush that suffused her face, she exuded beauty even as she denied it. "And heaven knows I'm not pretty."

"You couldn't prove that by me," I said.

"Oh, go on, now," she sobered then and continued. "I wasn't as pretty as I thought, and by the time I was forty-five I had to come to terms with that and accept it. Now I have to come to the fact of and accept my mortality. My two sisters dying in the past three years was painful. Those deaths, and seeing my other sister lying helpless in her bed at the rest home, slapped me in the face with the fact that I was mortal. It was hard, but I think I've now accepted it."

She began to rock, slowly, and I could imagine her as she was twenty-eight years before when I first had her as a teacher. She had been only two years older than I was now and had come to terms by then with the fact that she was not a pretty woman. I don't know about her coming to terms with a half-truth, nor why she hadn't married. I don't know if she had loves or lovers, been delivered broken promises, or had heartbreaks. But whatever had deprived her of a lasting mature love, it was now too late for her to experience it. She would be gone, perhaps in a year, or five years, maybe ten. Her bursitis and arthritis would take more of their toll and she would fade. But it occurred to me that she had fulfilled something of a need for love. There were so many children she had intellectually nurtured and, in return, gained love's satisfaction.

She leaned forward, her elbows resting on the oak arms of her solid rocker, a twinkle in her eye and a precise lilt in her voice. "But now, Clifton, there are some advantages to growing old. You can speak your mind without getting a poke in the nose." She laughed. "Who's going to fight with someone with so much gray in their hair?"

"Ruth, I won't fight with you even with gray in your hair. I suspect you're still pretty tough."

She laughed. "That's not how I remember you. You could be a pill. Do you recall that time you were talking in study hall and I demanded an apology which I never got?"

"I still say I was definitely not talking, at least not at the time you accused me."

"Yes, and you refused to apologize, and I told you not to come back to class until you did. Every day for two weeks you would walk into my room, stony-faced and not looking at me."

"And every day you would invite me to leave. I had to sit outside the home economics class and eat those cookies the girls baked and sneaked out to me."

"You finally came to me and said you would not apologize for something you hadn't done, but that you really wanted back in class." She shook her head looking as perplexed as she had the day I had gone in to her. I could still picture her sitting in the hard, oak desk chair with her chin in her palm, her eyes thoughtful as she tried to think of what would be best, then saying, "Clifton, I expect you to set an example in my class. There are a lot of the boys and girls in the lower grades who look up to you. I'm going to let you come back into the class because I don't think it's good for the others to see you lounging around by the home economics class eating cookies. But I want you to know, I still think you were out of line and should apologize to me. You disappoint me. And, if it happens again, I expect you to apologize or you will certainly never come back into my classroom." With that she'd dismissed me with a wave of her hand.

"And if I am out of line, I will apologize," I countered as I turned on my heel and stalked out. But a truce was made and I never crossed her again.

"You know, Ruth, I do really want to apologize now, but I still feel like an adolescent kid who can't swallow my pride and do it. Besides, I wasn't talking."

Ruth laughed again and laid a hand on mine. "We are both still too bullheaded, I guess, because I still think you were, and still stick by my threat, I won't let you come back to my class if it happens again." Her eyes glinted wickedly and she squeezed my hand. "But enough of that. I have some things I want to ask you. Now I don't want you to think I'm prying into your business but I want you to tell me some things about yourself. For instance, tell me, did you get through your training owing a lot of money?"

I felt a little uncomfortable with her question but I assured her that with the help of my wife, Carolyn, I had managed to support myself through all college and nine postgraduate years, and that I had never been in hock to anyone.

Ruth nodded in decided approval, then turned pensive. "My father was Irish and my mother was Pennsylvania Dutch. We were poor, Clifton. But mind you, we didn't know we were poor. My mother knew how to handle money. We were never in debt and we never borrowed money. Now I know that sometimes you have to borrow money to make money, but these days it's just too easy to borrow for all those frills that one can do without. My mother even gave us clothes and things we needed for Christmas. My father gave us books." Her eyes sparkled and I knew she prized her father's extravagance. "I'm happy to know you and Carolyn paid for it yourselves and could put off till later these extras that most people today can't seem to do without.

"But tell me about your family and about your work. Do you work for a clinic or are you in private practice? You have two sons. How are they doing? Is your practice a success? Are you still married?"

My children were doing well. My practice was doing well and I was my own boss. I had not divorced. She knew these were personal things she asked, she admitted it, and I'm sure she was not motivated by idle curiosity, so I answered her freely. She seemed to be trying to fill in some composite picture of me, perhaps an ideal she had of me, and now she was going to determine if I had "made it" by her standards. The way she smiled and nodded as I spoke showed she approved and it made me happy. I was sure, too, that anything I told her would remain between her and me, that I would not be the object of idle gossip.

I was even more assured of that when she went on to tell me about moving into town from the farm. She had lived for twenty-five years on her own land, with only her dog and livestock. Three years previously she lost her sister who lived close by and then not long afterward had broken her leg. "Fear and loneliness drove me to town.

"When I moved into town, I received a call from one of the ladies I know inviting me to play bridge. Clifton, I told her straight out that I was not going to do it. I didn't want to have to make excuses every time someone called for me to play. I had already joined clubs and played all the bridge I wanted to play. So, I told her, 'I appreciate your calling, Gussie, but I won't be playing any bridge or joining any sewing circles.' I can sew without sitting around with a bunch of chit-chatting women. And you know, Clifton, that's one of the main reasons I don't want to join those clubs; I don't like to sit around and gossip."

And it struck me that we had spent a lot of time talking and there had been no gossip.

Ruth sat there for a moment looking out from beneath her heavy gray eyebrows and I could remember when she sat at her desk with chalk in one hand and an eraser in the other explaining some math problem to her class. She would sit there poised on the edge of her chair, ready to push up and attack the blackboard with numbers and Xs and Ys if we did not have a look of comprehension in our eyes. She had sometimes reminded me of a determined and thoughtful bear as she wheeled around up and out of her chair and began to chalk furiously on the board. There was a no-nonsense attitude about her and I could still see it. She would not waste her time on idle chatter in the local sewing circles. She preferred to sit quietly knitting and sewing, or cleaning, washing, and grinding her own wheat flour so she could bake bread. And here in town she did not feel as keenly the dread of being isolated.

I did wonder about her fear, and told her I could not imagine a World War II army W.A.C. (Women's Army Corps) sergeant like her being afraid.

"Clifton, I had never been afraid before, not of any human being. But after my sister died, I went over to her house to put things in order. Back home again I walked in the front door and started back into the bedroom. And Clifton, I saw the bathroom door close. I want to tell you, I felt my heart stop." She gave a nervous laugh as she put her hand to her bosom in a gesture of alarm. She seemed to be reexperiencing that incident again right here in her own safe living room. "Well, I didn't know what to do. I knew there was someone in that bathroom and I felt fear. It was the first time I ever felt fear, Clifton. I didn't know whether to turn and run or back out the door. Well, I backed out of there and drove over to my neighbors'. They got their guns and we came back but I stayed in the car while they went in. They saw the bathroom door close, too, but there was no one there." Ruth laughed heartily. "It was only the draft coming through when the front door opened that caused it to close."

"But I want you to know, Clifton, that I have been afraid since then." She told me, her eyes turning down and her brow furrowing. "I had lived alone twenty-five years out on my farm and now I was afraid. Then, after I broke my leg, I decided I had to live in town so I bought this place, and I guess I'm glad, though it can never be home to me like my farm."

It was getting along in the afternoon by then and Ruth reminded me I had to get going if I was to make the reunion. I told her that I planned to skip the reunion and make the three-and-a-half-hour pilgrimage back to Chicago. "I have no real friends in the group," I said, "and some I don't even remember."

"Clifton, we are lucky if we have two or three real friends in a lifetime," she said.

I had also heard this from C. V. Ramana, my first teacher of psychoanalysis, or perhaps from Bernard Kamm or Elsie Haug, my analysts. It seemed peculiar to hear it from my maiden high school math teacher.

"I have to say I have been lucky; I have had my three or four friends. So, I'm not going to complain if I'm a little lonely now and then. I keep busy and that helps. And I remember that Jimmy Courts and you were good friends in high school."

"Jimmy Courts was a friend but not really a long-lasting one. All the others will be strangers."

She said, "You came here from so far away, have done things no one else who remained here has done. You should stay and share that with these people. Now promise me you will."

I promised I'd not vanish in the direction of the airport, but that I'd go to the reunion and come back next day to spend more time with her.

Ruth was an early riser and she greeted me next morning with a smile and a steaming cup of black coffee.

I told her that Evelyn Westfahl had not remembered me, actually even ignored me. "It was so strange because she was someone I could never forget. I wanted so badly to go out with her my junior year, and after she led me to believe she might, she chose the quarterback."

"It's a shame, Clifton, to not be recognized by her and then ignored. And it's understandable that you wanted so badly to date her in high school. She was quite the popular girl. It makes me remember things I really believed I wanted badly when I was younger. Now, I no longer want them. I'm even better off for not ever having a good many of them. I'd say to myself, if only I could have had a new car instead of that old 1936 Ford. But now, I really don't care if I have a new car or not." Ruth's gaze turned inward for a moment but she brightened again. "You're lucky you didn't get some of those girls like Evelyn that you thought you couldn't live without when you were seventeen. A boy of that age really doesn't look much further than skin deep."

"My mother used to say that beauty was only skin deep when I'd tell her about a particular girl I didn't think was pretty. I would sass her back and say if she skinned the girl first, I'd go with her."

Ruth laughed. "Now that wasn't very nice. I wouldn't have thought that of you."

"Willadean certainly wasn't one of the ones I thought needed skinning," I said and then went on to tell Ruth of one of my classmate's negative assessment of Willadean the first time I told him I'd like to date her.

Screwing his face up in disgust, he'd said, "Willadean? Willadean? You want to go out with Willadean?"

"That kept me from ever asking her for a date."

Ruth was thoughtful for a moment. "Well, Clifton, Willadean was the youngest of a big family, and they were all boys except for her. I think it just took her longer to mature than the other girls. She also liked working in the fields with her brothers and most of the girls around here didn't do that. But of all the girls in that class, she's the one I call a friend. She comes over and visits with me while we both knit. And we can work not saying a word for hours. She's not one to gossip or carry tales either. So, I guess, Clifton, you should have used your own good judgment and not that of someone else."

"Yesterday at the reunion he denied he ever said it."

"Time does do funny things to some people's memories, Clifton. They want to remember the past in ways that put them in a good light, not admit to their mistakes. There are a lot of people around here who do awful things, then try hard to make you see them in a good light. Are you a religious man, Clifton?"

I reddened and told her, "No, I set religion aside long ago."

"I'm not so sure about that, Clifton. Religion is not just going to church. There are a lot of people who call themselves religious that I don't think are at all. There's a married man, they tell me, who gets up before the congregation when the preacher's away and gives the most beautiful sermons you've ever heard. But he's been sleeping with another woman for years. Now him I don't consider religious. You? All I know about you convinces me you are a moral man even though you don't practice a creed. You have to realize that you are an exceptional person. There was something about the hardships you suffered as a boy that affected you positively."

I was glad she didn't really know everything about me. I knew that having left the strictness of this conservative community, that there were things I had done that she might disapprove of, but I didn't enlighten her. Ruth had believed in me then, and she still believed in me and, for the most part, I wanted her trust in me to remain. She was one of the most important mentors I was privileged to have in my lifetime and would always be an unforgettable part of my life.

It came time for me to leave, and Ruth began to shower me with gifts. First was an afghan she had spent hours knitting, then four loaves of bread she had made from her own wheat, washing the grain, grinding it, and baking the loaves. She even had pickle relish for which my mother had given her the recipe, and she wanted me to have some. I felt greedy accepting all these things, and I said, "Ruth, you have given me so much already. You don't have to give me more. I should be giving to you and here you are still giving to me." I said this as I stood in the doorway to the garage and watched her bustle about to bring loaves of bread and jars of pickle relish to me. I caught myself leaning against the door jamb with my hand in my pocket and remembered the days of "lounging around" I had done in the hallways and classrooms where Ruth had spent her adult life giving of her knowledge and understanding. It really should be my turn to give.

"You are giving to me, Clifton. You know, this is what my life is all about. It's the people who I've taught that make my life worthwhile." She turned and her eyes glistened with a promise of tears. I recalled she had told me earlier that when Bobby, one of my classmates, shot himself in the leg, she had not gone to see him. "I would have cried if I'd gone and nobody had ever seen me do that. I figured I didn't want them to start. So, I waited to see him till I knew I wouldn't cry and I cried before and after I went to see him." She might cry when I left her, too, but if she did, I wouldn't see her and the illusion could remain, my good, strong teacher of Pennsylvania Dutch stock who was strong, who cherished my friendship.

I hugged her and left.

I drove by the small bungalow I had called home for the three years I lived in Okeene. Many of the green asbestos shingles I had helped my stepfather cover the outside of the house with were cracked and some had fallen away. The front porch swing still hung from the rafters and a pleasant Mexican lady was sitting there swinging. She was very polite when I told her this had been my home, and she invited me in to see it, but I declined. It would seem too strange to go in and see things changed; different furniture, pictures, the knick-knacks. I'd be too sad if I saw that. I sat on the stoop for a few minutes and chatted, listening to her lamenting that the two run-down and deserted houses on the block were such a disgrace.

"The owner should do something with them," she said. "But she won't."

"Who owns them," I asked.

"An old high school math teacher named Ruth Addis," she said.

On the ride back to Chicago I thought about the paradoxes my trip to the reunion had presented me. With no solid reason or wish to attend, I had gone because I'd received an invitation and wanted only to see my old teacher. I had rationalized and excused myself for not remembering one of the people I saw at the reunion but been terribly upset at not having been remembered. I'd been told by Ruth that I had seen and experienced so much more than those who had remained behind in Okeene. I'd listened to the insights of my high school teacher who had been wonderful to me and had what I considered to be an abundance of wisdom, then found she owned two community eyesores and would do nothing to remove them. I wanted to ask her about that. But I couldn't.

Ruth died three years later without my ever seeing her again.

THE GYPSY

Were my experiences in Baltimore mundane or did they take on meaning only because I had traveled to this city to celebrate my acceptance into the professional ranks of the American Psychoanalytic Association? Much of what happened to me over a few days' time seemed charged with meaning and evoked in me the belief that they were unusual experiences, however mundane they might have seemed at another time. Meeting the beautiful gypsy, which occurred toward the end of my stay, was one such event. This meeting took place after having several others which I will only enumerate; I'd been publicly acknowledged as a certified member of the American Psychoanalytic Society; had cracked open and eaten fresh steamed crabs with Peter Blos, Jr. whom I mistook for his distinguished psychoanalyst father; surrounded by steely eyed secret service guards, I had been present at a speech given in my hotel by Jimmy Carter, the soon-to-be president of the United States. Now, after spending a day attending meetings and trying to absorb the ideas, theories, and solid clinical material presented, my head was stuffed full, I was off to see *The Cherry Orchard* where I would see the gypsy.

My driver was a taciturn fellow wearing a leather, billed cap. As another evening pushed away the warm spring day, I settled back in a cracked vinyl seat and watched out the window as we silently moved away from the hotel. I did not feel inclined to engage him in conversation, but as he sped up Charles Street, I noticed a large, marble Doric pillar that seemed to lie directly in our path. As the street split and we passed to the side of the monument, I asked what it was.

"I think it's the Washington Monument," he answered tersely, then resumed his silence. I learned later that, indeed, it was a monument to our first president, and the first one in this country that was approved for construction. My driver remained sullenly quiet as he drove to Baltimore's historic Mt. Vernon Cultural District, which sat alone in the middle of a wasteland. In 1974 an arson fire had burned its North Avenue location to the ground. Now the theater was located in a new space carved out of an abandoned Jesuit college, an ancient and massive building which had surrendered a small corner to the arts. As we drove toward that corner in the spring of 1976 it was a lighted beacon in its dark and empty environs.

Its dreary location was a fitting arena in which to stage a Russian playwright's work, and I looked forward to acquainting myself with this Chekhov play. Ten years earlier, I had been introduced to Russian literature by Ramana, the mystical Indian analyst who had mentored me during my residency in Oklahoma. He had mentioned that Dostoyevsky was considered by Freud to be a great writer and one who deeply understood the psychology of the human mind. Armed with that knowledge, I had bravely tackled "The Brothers Karamazov." My continued engagement with the four brothers in that patricidal opus proved to be too great a challenge and I had to put them aside for several years before I again approached those grim characters. I was not unimpressed by them, only overwhelmed. The feeling was not unlike what I'd experienced with Ramana when he first began to force me to look more closely at the frightening facts of depth psychology. My college education had not included many of the great writers, and it was only after my Chicago renaissance that I undertook and finished all of Dostoyevsky's writings, then Tolstoy's, then Chekhov's. Somehow, I'd missed seeing any of Chekhov's dramas, and now I would see *The Cherry Orchard* here at the Center Stage Theater. I looked forward to the evening little knowing that not all the drama would occur on stage.

Alighting from the cab after giving the cabbie only a minimum tip, I had been offended by his taciturn manner, I entered the front door to be pleasantly surprised. The timbers of the inner structure reminded me of a venerable, old oak table that had been scrubbed clean with PSP to remove all the grime and age-cracked varnish. The brick had been left raw and exposed, but it, too, was immaculately clean.

My arrival was well before the show began and, as I entered the building the heavy aroma of coffee drew me to a room decorated in many shades of brown accented by shiny copper fixtures and fittings. Chocolate-colored beams crossed high above the floor, and the bar-front was so like lightly-shaved chocolate that I could imagine licking my tongue across its smooth surface. The tile floor was the color of cardamom. Small, copper-coated tables were crowded into a postage stamp-sized space that was reduced further by four to six people squeezed around each, their knees pressed together and their heads shifted forward, as the angry gurgling of a large copper machine and its occasional, prolonged nasty hiss of relief drowned out their conversation. A hand-printed menu boasted hard liquor, wine, beer, hot chocolate, and something I'd never heard of before—cappuccino.

Cappuccino? I had no idea what that was. A tall, strikingly beautiful, African American woman operating the imposing, copper espresso machine smiled when I said, "I don't know what that is, but it smells so good I'd like one. Could you tell me what it is?"

"Strong coffee, cardamom, whipped cream, shaved chocolate, milk, and a cinnamon stick," she said.

"Alcohol?" I didn't want alcohol; I didn't like the way it made me feel.

"No alcohol," she said as she leaned on the counter, bringing her large, black eyes level with mine with a gaze so intent I blushed. "But it's really good."

I couldn't hold her gaze but said, "Give me one," and when I looked up again, she had turned to her cranky machine and was busy with its knobs and nozzles. Done, she sat the cup down in front of me and said, "That'll be two dollars, please." Her smile made me blush again.

Taking one sip, I was addicted and an espresso maker has since that moment never been absent from my kitchen.

Taking another sip of the near-scalding drink, I moved to the wall and stood leaning against the sandblasted, raw brick wall observing those around me, eavesdropping and savoring my cappuccino. Men in business suits sipped scotch. Young, avant-garde intellectuals in beards, jeans, and long-sleeve dress shirts swigged beer and stared, a bit too loutishly, at three pretty, full-bodied women just out of adolescence who spoke animatedly as they stood close together in a small group. Two handsome lesbians held hands across the coppery surface of one of the tables. Husbands and wives strolled about, nodding pleasantly to acquaintances. One pair stopped and engaged another in a discussion of the poor reviews *The Cherry Orchard* had received from the local newspaper critics. Two matronly women stood close to one side of me stirring their overheated cappuccinos with cinnamon sticks before taking a small, experimental sip and quickly lowering the cups to rub their smarting lips with tips of tongues.

On the other side of me, an overly large man in a Brooks Brothers suit held court with a small group standing close around him. "I think they are trying much too hard to educate the public and, instead, they had better strive to entertain the public. If they don't, they won't have any public." Nods of agreement all around, as I wondered who "they" were. He was not finished. "Chekhov alone would be okay but when he's followed by three other heavies, Shakespeare, Shaw, and Samuel Beckett—well—that's too much." He then breathed in deeply, expanding his chest in what I thought must be pride as the others agreed and I had the fantasy that he was going to continue to expand like a gaseous balloon and float away. I wondered if he were the one who wrote the poor review of *The Cherry Orchard*.

On the way back to the counter, I walked past a young man sitting cross-legged on the floor poring over an anthology of Russian plays. Had he come to contrast and compare? He was too engrossed to notice that I had paused to see what he was reading. As I stood there, empty cup in hand, I heard a grand old dame, leaning on her cane, addressing three older women who had arrived in the cab just in front of mine. In a clear and precise manner, like an orator giving a graduation speech, she said, "The Offstage Theater was an attempt to reintroduce theater to Baltimore. I think no better choice of directors could have been made than Jacques Marchetti. Baltimore City must be reclaimed from the urban blight into which it has sunk. I think this is just one of many successful ventures in that direction." She smiled a sad memory smile, and I imagined her seeing a childhood home in bygone days when Baltimore was strong and thriving. Or perhaps it was a visionary smile, a smile of hope for a future she would never see. I turned to the counter, handed over my cup, and ordered another cappuccino.

Just after taking the first cautious sips, the lights began to flicker signaling us to our seats. Hoping to finish my coffee, I held back until most of the audience had disappeared into the theater and then, along with a few other tardy drinkers, faced the theater entrance, took one step, and then, stopped as if on command—and stared.

From out of the night's growing darkness, an exotic vision swept into our midst. Not one male present in the room failed to pause, to find his eyes drawn like to a magnet to the dusky woman in bangles who, in a blue-and-red gypsy gown that swirled about her perfect ankles swept into the room. Gold hoops dangled from her ears and every finger was encircled in silver, gold, or platinum and, on their surfaces, multicolored stones gleamed and sparkled. I was most enchanted by the silky, dark tresses tumbling from beneath a fortune teller's kerchief and falling in elegant disarray over her shoulders, around her face, and halfway down her thighs. As a young adolescent I claimed as a girlfriend the one with the longest hair. This one I would have truly chosen. Framed by long, fluttery eyelashes, her black eyes flashed about the room as if she were seeing everyone and everything in a single glance. They seemed to rest on mine for a fraction, and I smiled at her. To my surprise her full, painted lips parted in a return smile and she nodded before those eyes swept on to another, then another, leading all the male egos to swear this beautiful and mysterious woman had singled them out for appraisal. Or so I imagined. Jealous wives would have a thing or two to say to their husbands about the raw lust burning in their eyes as they followed the gypsy into the theater. I was glad Carolyn had not been there to observe my own heated stare.

The lights dimmed as I hurried to the assigned seat, my eyes falling on the gypsy's long tresses for a fleeting moment before they blurred and disappeared into total darkness. As the curtain rose to disclose Lopakhin and Dunyasha awaiting the arrival of Ranevsky, I found the scene so suffused with energy that every line spoken was perceived as directed only to me, and I disregarded the reality of the crowd sitting about me.

The scene moved on, the drama unfolded, characters developed, and new characters stole into scenes. An era of Russian history was coming to an end and the director, despite what the critic had opined, was helping me experience it. I had felt a special kinship for Chekhov when I underwent a late renaissance on moving to Chicago. We had both grown up on farms and in small towns or villages located in provincial areas of our respective countries. Both of us had become physicians, he a general practitioner and I a psychiatrist, both of us with a wish to alleviate suffering in our fellowmen. His father and mine had striven to extricate themselves from their own kind of serfdom, each in his own way, and both had failed. We'd both experienced firsthand the raw, moist smell of earth turned by the plow, the grunts and steady syncopated hoof beats of horses as they labored. We'd both known the almost unbearable cold bite of winter and the scalding of a summer's noonday sun. He had lived, practiced medicine, and written plays and short stories during the time that my great-grandfather was teaching school in the Oklahoma Indian Territories. I too aspired to be a writer.

There was no intermission between the first and second act, but dim lights came on and bathed the theater in a hazy glow, and I let my gaze wander to the gypsy who sat looking back as if searching for someone behind her in the audience. Her eyes caught mine once more and held as she smiled, but the strains of Yepikhodov's guitar wafted through the dimming lights and her head snapped around to the stage just before all went dark.

I had trouble concentrating on the first moments of the play as I recovered from the disquiet the gypsy's smile had thrust upon me.

Did she think she knew me? That I was some long-ago acquaintance from high school? Was she attracted to me in some way? The thought made the blood rush to my face and I thought it a wonder that the area around me didn't light up from its glow. My first and second nights in Baltimore had been surprising and unexpected; why not believe that a gypsy might know me? I pushed these thoughts away and concentrated on the play, and as it progressed began to realize that though Chekov had written *The Cherry Orchard* as a comedy, to me it was more a tragedy. Perhaps, I thought, it was because his portrayal of all the comic characters' follies wasn't exaggerated to the point of ridiculousness. They were laughable but much too humanly tragic. Sometime later I thought about what I had experienced in Baltimore, and wondered about writing of it. Would it be a short story? A novel? A play? Would it be comedy? Or something more melodramatic? Until recently, I never considered that it might be part of a memoir. I am fearful that critics will laugh unkindly when they read of my follies, of mistaking Peter Blos Jr. for his father, and my gawking at a gypsy woman, one that disappeared right after the lights came on when the second act ended.

I joined the slow-moving crowd flowing out into the lobby, the close bodies wafting odors of cologne, perfume, alcohol, and the rich smell of espresso coffee. The throng fanned out into the large open space, hurrying once they were free of the constricted opening out of the theater to line up for drinks or expresso. Before I could reach the espresso line, I was greeted by Jake, a colleague of mine, and his wife, Ella. I was introduced to his brother and sister-in-law and, as I shook hands all around, I detected a definite undertone of disquiet, but had no idea what was transpiring. Jake reminded me of a cross between the scarecrow and the tinman, two characters out of *The Wizard of Oz*. His suit was too short in the pant legs and coat sleeves, and his elongated face had the immobility of galvanized metal; his movements mechanical. What few times I'd spoken with him in the past, I'd felt uncomfortable as he always stood too close, much like a number of New Yorkers I'd known, invading my personal space. Ella and her sister were preoccupied and aloof, though polite.

When I told Jake I was there alone for the week, with obvious envy he exclaimed, "Down here for a whole week? God! That must be a treat to get away for a few days so you can live it up." He was oblivious to the look of hurt that passed over Ella's face.

The sister-in-law was quick to come to her sister's defense, saying, "I guess, Jake, we'll have to ship you to the North Pole where you can get away for a few days by yourself."

"I hear the Eskimo girls are okay once you get used to them," her husband quipped.

Trying to change the subject, I asked if they were enjoying the play, but before anyone could answer, the brother-in-law breathed out a sigh of disbelief and said, "Seven days. I can't believe it." He, too, seemed totally unaware of the anger flooding the two women's faces. Unable to bear the tension, I excused myself and walked over to the line waiting for cappuccino. As I walked away, I heard Jake say, "Having a good time in Baltimore for seven days!" I looked back and saw both men shaking their heads in disbelief at my good fortune, as their wives glared at them with undisguised venomous stares. Then everyone's attention was diverted by the momentary appearance of the gypsy who quickly disappeared into the theater for the third act.

The superb finale of Chekhov's drama, the passing of an age, the sound of axes taken to the ancient cherry trees which had existed through generations of nobility, the death of Firs, the last serf, gripped my imagination. I forgot Jake and Ella, the sister and brother-in-law and the gypsy woman as the laughter, the tears, the fond reminiscences, the bitterness, and the hope played out to the end. On leaving the theater, the images of the old forgotten servant crawling into a child's bed to die and the sound of axes biting into cherry wood followed me out into the night. Those events signaled the beginning of a new era, an era I'm sure Chekhov could scarcely have imagined. To me the play had special significance because I knew I had come to the end of an era as well and could identify with each of the parts played across the stage as the drama progressed, each characterization matching in some way, small or large, the moods I'd felt of late. Like Trofimov I had been the perpetual student. Like Lopatin, at times obsessed with money, and in my attempts to understand psychoanalytic theories, as clumsy as Yepihodov. Sentimental as Madam Ranevskaya, I shed tears at times when giving up some cherished ideas of my past while in search of something more reasonable to guide my future. And I was as idealistic as Anya, and in my concern about passing through my fourth decade and into the fifth, as vain as Yasha. And like these characters I was too often wrapped up in concerns about the past and future while neglecting the present. But tonight Chekhov had made me aware of the changes my trip to Baltimore symbolized and how I felt about it right now.

I would never need to be in any kind of training or schooling again. I was a certified psychoanalyst. I was exhilarated, but at the same time, I felt loss, a sadness, and an uncertainty about the future. There were now no clear goals for me to strive for, and I had to step into an adult role different from any I'd played before. There was no one to teach me, supervise me, and guide me. I was on my own.

Engaged in these thoughts, I stepped out onto the curb to hail a cab and saw the elderly women who had arrived as I did. They stood expectantly at the curb, waiting for the taxis both they and I had assumed would appear after the show. During the next few minutes, the crowd all walked down the block and across the street to a parking lot where their cars awaited them. They soon disappeared, leaving us waiting at the curb to slowly realize no cabs were going to appear to whisk us away to our hotel. I reassured my companions that I would find us transportation and walked to the door of the theater. It was locked. No one answered when I knocked, then pounded my fist on the door. The building and all the area around it for blocks were deserted and isolated. There would be no cabs and, in this industrial area, there would be no lighted windows of homes where I could hope to ask for the use of a phone. A picture of the area around our hotel I'd seen the night I'd arrived came to me, a picture of mean streets with police and guard dogs patrolling. There were no police here. It was a spooky and deserted part of the city. Even the street lights were widely spaced, and threw sickly shadows out of which I could imagine danger emerging.

I returned to the women and told them of our predicament, but reassured them I would go in search of help some ten blocks away where there was a busy street. They looked so frightened, these three aging ladies huddled together on this now darkened street, that I wondered if they thought I would abandon them as well. I assured them as best I could and hurried to the corner, where I was able to observe a distant area of the parking lot. Four people were still standing under a lone street light exchanging good-byes, ready to enter their cars and drive away. I ran full out, calling out for them to please wait. As I approached, I was greeted with stares of mild apprehension and distrust by the two men who had not yet entered their cars. But when I reached them the cautious looks disappeared. I'm sure I must have seemed more distraught than threatening. And I had on a suit and tie, which I'm sure made me less threatening.

"My companions and I seem to be stranded," I blurted out while still a few feet away, though having slowed to a walk, prepared to elaborate further as I caught a deep breath, but at that moment, from what I now saw was a gold Cadillac, there emerged the gypsy with all her spangles and bangles and a look of concern on her lovely face. I stammered and stumbled for words as I explained the predicament the ladies and I found ourselves in.

"This is certainly no place for you to get stranded," the gypsy said, surprising me somehow that she spoke in a well-modulated, intelligent, and sophisticated voice. There was no trace of the exotic that I had expected, no Bohemian accent, no silky flow of mysterious words. "Go reassure those poor ladies and we'll drive by and pick you up." She smiled and extended her invitation without consulting the man with her, then settled into the Cadillac's driver's seat as I hurried away at a fast walk, relieved but slightly amused that the gypsy's ride was not the covered wagon pulled by two weary horses that I'd imagined but a Cadillac with hundreds of horsepower under its hood.

I gave a thumbs up as I approached the ladies, and their anxious brows lost their troubled frown. I wondered what they were going to think when they realized they were being rescued by a gypsy. Would they weigh the hazard of riding in a Cadillac with a gypsy stranger at the wheel against that of waiting on a dark street in Baltimore while I went to fetch a cab? I thought not. Had the gypsy been riding in a brightly painted two-horse wagon, I don't think any of us would have failed to huddle together in the back among all her arcane belongings and relatives. When the gypsy executed a wide U-turn and came to rest at the curb, we did not hesitate to pile in and huddle together in the back seat, which, though wide, was not made to accommodate four people. My companions were quick to voice their gratitude at our rescue, introduce themselves, and to engage our exotic hostess in conversation. I found that the three were wives of prominent, nationally known psychoanalysts, the names of whom I can no longer recall, though I was impressed with their names at the time

The real surprise came when our gypsy benefactor told us who she was.

THE GYPSY

She was no ordinary person, this gypsy who had taken the reins, or at least the steering wheel, of our golden conveyance; this gypsy was the Director of Mental Health for the state of Massachusetts!

The gracious gypsy mental health director delivered us to our door and, as we stood outside the hotel watching her drive away, one of the rescued women said, "Well, I would never have thought to have a gypsy running the state mental health program, but that was one gypsy that would get my vote."

"Mine too," I said.

THE WOMAN IN THE MIRROR

Wayne Miller turned off U. S. 90 and shortly arrived at the edge of Pickerton, a remote village lying in a corner of Ohio. He'd reluctantly made a reservation at the Riverside Bed and Breakfast, a small place hidden away well off the main highway. Five years ago, while driving back from Niagara Falls after celebrating their tenth anniversary, Wayne and his wife, Samantha, had spent the night there in a quaint B&B. Pickerton had been so much quieter and more enjoyable than Niagara Falls with its elbow-to-elbow tourists and a honeymoon suite decorated with the gaudiness of a cheap bordello. Last week when Samantha had impulsively decided they should come here for their fifteenth, he'd protested, "I can't leave my laboratory dogs in the hands of that sophomore lab assistant. He'll screw up."

Her pretty blue eyes had flashed anger. "Those damn dogs are more important than me."

"That's ridiculous. It's just that those damn dogs are the heart of my research." He wished that were really the reason he didn't want to leave. But it wasn't. For the last five years, things had been strained between them. He couldn't figure it out, but he had been moody and emotionally unavailable much of the time, and worked long hours. He slept poorly and had disturbing dreams, some phantom woman roaming through his restless slumber. He'd awaken sweating from nightmares. He and Samantha had drifted further and further apart. She slept in the guest bedroom sometimes, and was short tempered with him. "Look, I love you, not my dogs."

"Good. Then take me to the Riverside B&B for our anniversary."

"Don't you remember how skunk drunk we got there? It took us two days to recover."

Samantha shrugged. "What I remember most is how much fun we had before we got drunk. Then you started that love affair with your dogs and I don't think we've had much fun since."

He bristled at that, wanted to hit back with something hurtful. "And you opening up a new dress shop and spending evenings and weekends there has nothing to do with us not having fun anymore?"

"I don't want to fight anymore, Wayne. I just thought we might rediscover fun if we went there."

"Okay. Okay, we'll go." he said, but then felt a surge of unaccountable discomfort.

Now, coming to a stop in the parking lot of the Riverside B&B, he gazed out over the open meadow that lay behind it, surprised that for no good reason he could think of a hot flush spread over his cheeks. On the horizon a dark cloud partially hid the red glow from the setting sun. Grabbing their bags, he hurried Samantha inside, where they were greeted by a smiling, plump, fiftyish-or-so woman who led them to their room. "Enjoy your stay," she said, then quietly closed the door behind her.

"This is still so quaint. It's just like I remembered." Samantha raised her arms, twirled around once and fell onto the soft, flowered spread that covered the high poster bed.

With her slim body and long blond hair, she reminded Wayne of a wood nymph lying in a bed of flowers. The thought troubled him. A sinking feeling pulled at his gut as he surveyed the dressers, tables, and chairs on whose surfaces sat ancient artifacts he was sure had been handpicked from untold numbers of yard sales and antique stores. "It's nice," he equivocated. He had only a dim awareness that he had ever been here before. It surprised him how unfamiliar it seemed. How unsettling.

Samantha eyed him wearily. "Don't be so overenthusiastic," she said and stood. "Let's change and go to dinner at that little bar and restaurant we found last time. Maybe we can get drunk and have some fun."

The walk to the restaurant was familiar to Wayne in a macabre, dim way and the morose idea that it heralded disaster pulled at his consciousness as the waiter filled their wine glasses.

Samantha raised her glass. "To us," she said.

"To us," Wayne toasted. But he didn't feel anything for her. It was as if a part of him had decided to become dormant. Or dead. He thought of how almost everyone he knew believed Samantha and his union was blessed, that their life together had been a storybook tale. And it had been for a while; they'd grown together in that first ten years of marriage, appeared mostly happy. He'd finished his PhD in neurophysiology and landed a research position at Norrison University. Had gained a reputation in the department. There had been considerable praise of his meticulous attention to detail and creative grasp of writing research grants that ended up generously funded. All that didn't seem important now. And there was his prized other, Samantha, the beautiful and talented woman who had stepped back and forth between her life as a successful dress designer and the perfect hostess to his frequent departmental parties.

Startled, almost spilling his wine as his hand jerked, he was called back from his musing as a waitress eyed him with a puzzled frown. "I'm sorry, what did you say?" he asked the woman.

"You okay?" Samantha set down her wine glass, concerned lines crinkling at the edge of her eyes and forehead.

"I was just thinking about what you said, that the last time we were really happy together was here, five years ago. Just trying to figure out why it changed afterward."

Samantha shrugged. "We've both been busy. Stopped spending enough time together. Let's try to leave all that behind us tonight."

The bottle of light chardonnay consumed over too short a time lightened the mood and, after their meal, Wayne took Samantha to the piano bar, where they sang songs and danced to the music cheek-to-cheek. Being two of the few there, they had room to slowly move about on the postage-stamp-size dance floor, he somewhat plodding and she light on her feet. His earlier unease calmed until Samantha asked, "Remember the young woman we met last time we were here? I think the three of us got smashed together."

"I hardly remember," Wayne said, though something about that young woman tickled the back of his mind, frightening him. "Let's sit down for a minute."

Vague memories began floating into his mind of that night five years ago. He and Samantha had come here and danced and drank until both were giddy and mirthful. He now remembered there was a young woman, Desiree, who had joined them, confiding that she was to be married one month from their own wedding date. But she had argued with her fiancé that evening and come here, hoping he would show up later. As the evening drew near midnight, Desiree had become angrier with her fiancé and more provocative with Wayne, playing footsies with him under the table and pressing hard against him when they danced, arousing him. Samantha, deep into her wine glass, hadn't seemed to notice, but he'd felt guilty and ashamed that he was enjoying Desiree's attention.

Wayne now tried to push the memories out of his mind by downing a martini he'd ordered, had another and would have had still another, but the last of the dinner guests rose to leave and the pianist stopped playing. Very late, now, Samantha drove them back to their B&B and, though tipsy, upon reaching the door, Wayne lifted her into his arms and carried her across the threshold. Her head nestled into his neck. He tried to make love to her then, but an indistinct image of another woman blurred his vision, obscuring Samantha's face, deflating him. He rolled aside, then rose on one elbow and looked into her eyes, now clouded with hurt.

"I'm sorry, Samantha. I'm just too drunk."

She stroked his face. "I think you just had one martini too many. Don't worry about it." She snuggled close to him. "Let's get some sleep. Maybe tomorrow when we get over our hangover, you can do better." She was soon breathing deeply.

All Wayne could think to do was to say, "I'm really sorry," one more time.

He could not sleep; only doze off before coming awake again. In the middle of the night, his heart racing, he sat up, sweat blooming on his face and body. He'd imagined someone with long fingernails sitting in the room, tapping gently on a hard surface, and that he saw a woman's delicate hand, the fingers long and slim, reaching toward him, calling, "Help. Wayne. Wayne. Help. Wayne."

Coming fully awake he realized it was Samantha calling out, "Wayne."

He touched her shoulder. "Samantha, wake up. For God's sake."

Samantha's eyes opened and she stared at him as if he were a stranger. Recognition came slowly. "Wayne, I just had a horrible nightmare." Her mouth trembled and tears moistened her cheek.

"So did I. But it must have been because you were screaming my name."

"In the dream it was dark and I was alone in bed." Samantha said. "Some woman kept saying my name, over and over. And demanding, "Help me, Samantha. It was eerie."

"I thought someone was calling out too." He shivered.

Samantha reached out and stroked the back of his hand. "I'm sorry." She moved away from him then and turned on her side. "Let's go someplace fun tomorrow and not come back drunk," she said and once more settled into sleep.

His heart would not stop pounding. Beads of sweat ran down inside his pajamas. Unable to sleep, he rose, stumbled into the bathroom, and ran cold water over his face. As he raised his head and looked into the mirror, he stared, horrified. The ghostly face of a woman peered out from its glassy surface. He smelled gardenias.

Backing away, he stood shivering, smothered in the scent of gardenias, afraid that nothing would ever be the same again. He had heard of schizophrenia setting in without warning—one moment the person leading a near-normal life and then the next his life falling apart, visions coming, torturing ideas and agonizing feelings overburdening his sense of reality. Now it had happened to him, to a man who spent his days looking into the biochemistry of the brain, a man who was convinced that everything emotional and interpersonal had a neuro-biological causation. He stood, sweating, desperate, and hoping that the woman he saw gazing out at him with large, moist eyes would leave. Terrified, he looked away and thought of Natasha.

Natasha had given him a soulful look just before he'd anesthetized her and opened her calvarium to implant the electrodes. She seemed to know that there was something afoot and, in her dumb doggy way, she mourned his cold withdrawal from her, the distance he had to develop in order to pursue his experiment. He hated the dehumanized state he found himself in, the scientific remoteness with which he performed his surgeries on experimental animals, and then terminated their lives.

He dreaded looking up and seeing that the cold, hard surface of the mirror still held the soft lines of that face bathed in wistful vapor, but he slowly raised his head only to see his own haunted brown eyes regarding him. The lines at the corners of his eyes were deeper and his high forehead was wrinkled in distress. Gasping, he returned to bed; where he found Samantha still deeply asleep. For a long time, he lay staring at the dark ceiling, feeling exposed to those eyes in the mirror. He couldn't blow the scent of gardenias out of his nostrils, though he snuffed hard several times. Finally, he escaped into a foggy sleep.

On awakening two hours later, apprehensive and disorganized, he stumbled out of bed, dressed and made his way outside. He began walking toward a wooden fence at the end of the parking lot, his way lighted by a bright moon and, as he approached, he saw beyond it the small, open meadow, water from the river shimmering in the moonlight. Straddling the wooden rails, he felt drawn the hundred or so yards to the river's edge, where he stood looking out over the water. A dog, or perhaps a fox, barked. Faint images in the clear surface of the river reminded him of the strange vision in the mirror, haunting, ready to emerge into his new reality, more forerunners of madness. As he stood there, a thin, predawn mist rolled in from the river.

From downriver he heard someone call. "Wayne."

Startled, his first thought was that Samantha had awakened and was calling him, though he recognized that it was not her voice. Bathed in the gathering mists but still highlighted by the moon's glow, he saw a woman. She was standing in the water at the river's edge. The muted fragrance of gardenias enveloped him.

"Help me?" The call was insistent.

"Who are you? What do you want?" he yelled and started toward her. The smell of gardenias grew stronger as he came nearer. The hairs on his neck stood out and ice entered his spine as he approached close enough to see the woman who had sought him out in his mirror. He stopped, afraid to go any nearer.

She did not call again. Born by a light breeze that sprang up, a dense fog wafted in. Her ghostly figure appeared and disappeared as the fog swirled around her. Once again, she called, "Help me."

"Please, how can I help you?"

"Please, help me?" She called once more, unable or unwilling to say more. Like a crumpling sheet, she receded as the fog closed about her. He turned and fled to the room, where he sat through the remainder of the night gazing on Samantha, hoping her presence would keep him sane. She slept on as the sun rose, lighting the room.

Samantha's ruffled hair lay in golden strands across the pillow. Light and shadows played across her face, patterns created by gently fluttering leaves on the Honey Locust outside the window. Those warm designs also played on the naked skin of one leg that lay outside the sheet. Not wanting to startle her from sleep, but unable to be alone another second, he softly called her name. She stirred, then looked at him with sleep-distant eyes. With a start, she sat up, her face clouding in alarm.

"What's wrong?" She threw the covers back and came over to him. "Tell me what's wrong, Wayne."

"I didn't sleep. That's all. More nightmares. You know . . ." He left the sentence hanging; saw the dissatisfaction in her frown.

"Oh, God; you don't look well. Why don't you lie down for a while?"

"Look, Samantha, I just want to eat. Get dressed." He turned and walked to the bathroom to run water over his face. He did not look in the mirror.

She did not argue with him, but quickly dressed and walked downstairs with him to breakfast. As they waited for their eggs Benedict, she said, "Something's been nagging me since that dream. Five years ago, I was drunk out of my skull, and so were you. But I seem to remember that girl Desiree helping me get to bed and wanting me to help her. Do you remember that?"

"I don't remember anything after that third or fourth martini I had."

"I remember thinking the next morning that you'd fallen down on somebody's lawn. There were grass stains on your pants."

"I don't recall any of that."

"We left the next morning and you were in no condition to drive, I remember. But you insisted we go."

He felt uncomfortable again. "I sorta remember that." Their breakfast came, but Wayne felt queasy and just pushed a piece of Canadian bacon around on his plate. When Samantha had finished, he asked, "Shall we pack and go? This place seems to be creeping us out."

"Not right now. I want to get in a sauna and have a massage. Why don't you come too?"

"I need to walk." Leaving Samantha to the sauna and masseuse, he took off walking toward the downtown area. The sky had begun to darken with low-flying clouds. Hurriedly, as though afraid that if he moved more slowly, he would falter, he walked six blocks along tree-lined streets until he saw a building hidden on three sides by a grove of stately trees. The front steps were wide and the façade a mixture of gothic and baroque, its somber visage softened by cool shade. Letters chiseled into the stone archway proclaimed it to be the public library. Books and libraries were things that could calm him, so he ascended to the open oak doors. Inside he was surprised at the spaciousness and simplicity of the lighted, airy reading room flanked by tall stacks of books. It soothed him, lessened the night's terror, and spoke to him of a peaceful timelessness, of an interval uncluttered with fears of madness.

A pleasant looking, white-haired woman sitting at a large oak counter in the center of the room greeted him. "How may I help you, young man?"

It would have amused Wayne to have been so addressed had he not felt so anxious and ill at ease. Now his face hardened and he looked at the floor. He recalled his mother and how she had always called him "young man" when she was angry with him. He would walk in without closing the door behind him, and she would rebuke him, "Were you born in a barn, young man?" He read rebuke in this pleasant woman's request even as he realized there was no reason to think so.

"Thanks, but I just wanted to browse around."

"You're a stranger in town, aren't you?" the woman said with that special knowledge local people had of anyone who lived in and around the town and of strangers passing through.

"I am. My wife and I are staying at the Riverside B&B. We're celebrating our fifteenth wedding anniversary."

"How nice. But, why Pickerton? Niagara Falls isn't that far."

"Around this time five years ago we did go to Niagara. Didn't like it. But we stopped here on the way home and my wife loved it. Wanted to come back."

"Oh, dear. Five years ago, you said. That was when we had that awful tragedy here."

"Tragedy?"

"Yes. One of our very own's fiancée was drowned. Richard Peterson's." She leaned forward as if telling a secret. "They never knew if it was an accident or not."

Wayne felt weak-kneed and had to steady himself against the counter. "That's sounds just awful."

"Yes, it was. Nobody could figure out what she was doing down by the river in the middle of the night." She pursed her lips. "My son's one of the local sheriff's deputies and he told me she left The Applegate with a pair of strangers." The woman looked around as if to see if anyone was listening and said, "He said she'd had a little too much to drink."

"What was the poor woman's name?" Wayne's pulse quickened and he prayed it wasn't Desiree.

"I don't rightly recall. She was from over Elston way, about ten miles from here. Had only been in town less than a year."

"Sounds like quite a mystery." Wayne's throat tightened and he found it hard to breathe. Light-headed, he dug his nails into the palm of both hands, hoping the pain would clear his head.

"Oh, it was. We have all the old back newspaper files you could read to find out more, if you like."

Wayne tried to slow his breathing. He wanted to turn and leave, not find out what he dreaded he already knew. But he cleared his throat and, unable to speak, nodded.

"Let me show you how to use the computer. Everything is electronic now, you know."

The librarian smiled and, as she led him to a small room off the main floor, her gray curls dancing on her high neck, Wayne was reminded of the image of a Greek woman on a Grecian urn he'd once seen and that brought to his mind the Greek tragedies. He felt he was in the midst of a tragedy of his own.

"There's seventy years of newsprint stored here." She sat down, turned on a computer, scrolled through scores of menus, came up with one, and gave him the chair.

Taking her place, he found his voice again and said, "I'll take it from here, if you don't mind. I know how to use the computer." The desk sat near a large window looking out on a yard graced with stately oak and elm trees. Rain had begun to fall. From somewhere in the distance, a child's unhappy cry penetrated the woods, fading as it crossed the sill and touched his ear. He sat motionless, a pain stabbing him deep in his gut. The sudden sharp bark of a black dog chasing a squirrel that jumped into the golden boughs of the strange tree startled him but he forced his attention to the screen. He could not relax.

As he scrolled through the pages, unwilling to go directly to the last ones where today's date five years ago lay, he scrolled past a decade of files, the dates blinding him, shut out for a brief time anything viewed from within. He jerked, sending the cursor skidding wildly across the screen when a clap of thunder burst overhead. Settling himself, though his hands trembled, he scrolled down again until a date seized his attention. He clicked on it.

Tragedy Takes Bride-To-Be

Below the headline, a black-and-white picture showed a woman's solemn face, her gaze fixed on him. He moaned and closed his eyes. It was the same face that had invaded his mirror. He stood, the chair overturning behind him, and fled the library, a smell of gardenias hovering over his path, forcing him to struggle forward as though he were wading through honey made of gardenia nectar.

Running back toward the inn, he tripped over a broken piece of sidewalk and fell hard, bruising his hands, elbows, and knees, tearing the fabric of one shirt-sleeve and both pant legs. Stunned, he lowered himself to the sidewalk and turned on his back to let the rain wash over him as memory came roiling back, memory of that night five years ago. It was as if it were happening right now, him and Desiree helping a very drunk Samantha back to the hotel room and put her to bed.

As he and Desiree undressed Samantha, Desiree kept saying, "Samantha. Samantha. You have to help me, Samantha. Samantha?" She'd commanded, "Listen to me. Sit up now. Pull your arm out of the sleeve. Samantha? Help me." Samantha held her arms up and let Desiree peel her blouse away and pull off her skirt.

When Samantha was in bed and passed out, Desiree collapsed onto the couch and gazing up at Wayne with eyes the color of topaz, her lips slightly parted in a smile, said, "Let's sit for a minute," and then patted the seat beside her.

He remembered his heart speeding up and his groin tightening. In his drunken state, he had no business sitting down beside this beautiful woman. "I think not just now. It's late and I'm sloshed. And tired."

"Want to see me home, then?" She asked. "Or should I sleep on the couch?"

"Walking you home is the least I can do." He was not as drunk as Samantha, and thought he could manage to stay on his feet. He did not want Desiree here when he awoke next morning, sure Samantha would sense what he felt for the woman.

Desiree held a hand up and he took it, helped her rise to her feet. She stumbled against him and he grabbed hold of her waist to keep her from falling, or to keep from falling. Laughing at themselves, they left the house and weaved their way to the street. "I'm not sure we can walk much further," he said.

"We'll stagger, then," she said.

"How far is it?"

"Far enough. Let's cut through the meadow and walk the path by the river. It'll save ten minutes."

"In the dark? We'll fall in the river."

"Wayne. The moon's up and I know the way by heart. Could do it with my eyes closed and drunk."

A near-full moon flooded the meadow with light as they weaved and swayed down the path, the soft earth under their feet making no sound. The quiet was so complete it was eerie. "This is nothing like a night in a city," Wayne said. "No sirens, no cars and trucks rumbling by. Not even a dog barking."

"Only the river refuses to be quiet," Desiree said as they neared the water and its deep, rapid-flowing current let itself be heard. "Let's sit for a minute." Not waiting for a response from him, she folded her long legs beneath her and settled onto the grass.

Wayne stood over her, not sure what to do. He was light-headed, and he wanted to walk Desiree on home so he could lie down and sleep beside Samantha. She reached up and took his hand, tugged gently. He sank down beside her. "I'm not sure I'll be able to get back up."

"Me neither," she said. "But the night's warm. We can just sleep here." She giggled.

"What's so funny?"

"Here we are, you a married man and me a bride-to-be, and I'm talking about sleeping with you all night on a riverbank."

Wayne considered this before answering. "Maybe I'd better get up."

She stretched out and put her hands behind her head. "You're pretty uptight, aren't you?"

The sting of her remark cut through the drunken haze that threatened to overwhelm him. "I'm sitting here drunk on a riverbank with an attractive woman, aren't I?"

"Most of the men I know would have made a pass at me by now."

"You're drunk and mad at your fiancé. Otherwise you wouldn't talk like that."

She laughed and sat up. Leaning forward, she kissed him full on the mouth.

She smelled of gardenias and her mouth tasted of beer and something else, maybe steak sauce. Or hamburger. That clinical and distant thought was absent any passion, he thought. Why wasn't there at least a glimmer of desire? Maybe she was right; he was pretty uptight "I really must get back to Samantha," he said. But, when he tried to rise, she pulled him back and kissed him again before rolling away to the edge of the river. He tried to stand up, but his head spun and he lay back on the grass, closing his eyes. When he opened them again, Desiree was standing now, too near the edge of the river, staring at the water. Reflected in the moonlight, she glowed softly, reminding him of a beautiful ghost.

With dizziness receding to a monotonous ache between his eyes, he stood and walked unsteadily to her. "I'm sorry," he said, and put his arms around her. Over her shoulder he could see the river current rippling and shimmering.

"Shouldn't you go on back to your passed-out wife?" she asked, but, then turned and cuddled in to him.

"I don't know. Should I?" He kissed her, hard. She wrapped her arms around his neck and opened her mouth to his tongue. Heat suffused him as he pulled her body closer, but then he thought of Samantha. The giddiness returned and guilt constricted his stomach and chest. As he tried to move away, Desiree clung to him.

"Please," she said, plaintively, like a bereft little girl.

"I just can't." he took her arms from around his neck and pushed her away.

Desiree stumbled sideways and began to fall.

Wayne grabbed for her, missed and with frozen horror, heard her scream once before she splashed into the fast-moving current. Disappeared.

He looked for her, but saw only the glimmer of moonlight on the roiling water's surface. Then, from several yards downriver, he heard her scream again, "Help me, Wayne. Help me."

He ran along the bank, slipping and sliding, almost falling once, trying to glimpse her, not knowing what to do. When the cries for help ceased, he staggered and fell to his knees. His head in his hands, dizziness and nausea gripping him, he lay back, horror and guilt enveloping him.

Now the same awful sensations gripped him as he lay prostrate on the unforgiving concrete walk with the rain pelting his face. He wanted to cry, shriek, do something to quiet the screaming fear and guilt crowding his head and chest. He shuddered to think his mind had played such a trick on him, keeping that awful moment hidden away for five years.

A car slowed and someone shouted, "You okay?"

He picked himself up off the concrete, waved and shouted back. "I just slipped and fell. I'll be fine."

He wasn't fine; his knees were bloody and his left knee-cap pained him with each step as he limped slowly back to the B&B. Changed, thankful that Samantha was still at the pool and not asking what happened, he stuffed his torn shirt and trousers into his suitcase, packed his things and, composing himself as best he could, sat waiting for her to come back to the room. He sensed a presence hovering in one corner of the room.

Three months later Wayne leaned over one of his dogs, a female spaniel he had taken from the pound and the first to be used for his upcoming research on humans and dogs with brains damaged by lack of oxygen from strokes. He had to anesthetize the dog, and then block a major artery, causing stroke-like damage to her brain. He would then try to retrain the dog's brain to recover some or all the function that was lost. Then euthanize her and section the brain.

The dog lay quietly on the table, gazing up at Wayne with trust. He could not meet her eyes. Instead he looked across the room at the specter in the corner, the one that had followed him from Pickerton.

Desiree always stood nearby. She no longer called out to him, only drifted through his days and nights, ghosting with her large, misty eyes beseeching, haunting him.

The spaniel's whimper startled him and, when she nuzzled his hand, he wanted to cry. Samantha had packed up weeks ago and left for her parents' home. She said she wasn't planning on coming back.

"I can't go on living with someone who's never present, even when he's in the same room with me," she'd said, not knowing they were not alone.

The spaniel huffed a low, quick bark and wagged her tail; her soulful eyes seemed full of sorrow for him.

He just could not continue the experiment, so he sat her on the floor and led her back to the kennel, Desiree floating on before them.

He locked the kennel door and climbed the stairs to the building's roof where he could see miles in all directions. Climbing onto the concrete wall that edged the roof, he could make out the house he'd shared with Samantha. The faint bark of a dog sounded from below and he peered down at the green lawns and shrubbery, the small creek that meandered through the far corner of the grounds.

Desiree floated into view a few feet in from of him and hovered, suspended on air. She nodded, beckoned to him, then dispersed like early mist giving way to late morning sunlight.

TENNESSEE MAN

Jack Wolfson towered over most men and, with a full, white beard that fluffed out halfway down his chest and silvery hair down past his shoulders, he could readily play the role of Santa, or, as happened on occasion at church, be mistaken for a biblical character and thus completely awe impressionable youngsters. He'd heard one six-year-old boy ask his mother in a stage whisper, "Is that Moses?" And, on another occasion he'd heard a five-year-old girl exclaim, "Is that God?" Though a descendant of Tennessee mountain forebears who ran distilleries and delivered whiskey outside legally licensed venues, Jack had never dabbled in the making and selling of white lightning but had played the role of Santa many times. He never pretended to be Moses or God; he'd left those roles to Charlton Heston and George Burns.

He had, for many years, played the role of troubleshooter for large companies in need of someone with down-to-earth good sense; someone who could restart complex computers or rewrite computer programs that weren't working for reasons too complicated for others to understand; or equally adept at such a simple task as plugging in a mainframe computer that a company technician refused to consider doing because, "No one ever unplugs that machine." No one, that is, except on one occasion when a maid needed an outlet for her vacuum and on another when a contractor needed to plug in his electric drill.

Lured away from Los Angeles, California, by Paul Anderson, the owner of a small, but growing software company, he'd moved to Tennessee, not far from where he'd grown up as a boy. Jack's one stipulation was that he would only take the position if guaranteed that he would not have to write reports. Anderson agreed and assured Jack that he would have a relatively free hand—and receive a hefty raise in salary. Jack bought a country home that prior to the Civil War had been a stopping-off place for the underground railroad.

Five months later, Anderson sold his business to a larger company and a new manager was installed. After the transition to new management, Anderson departed, and during the first week and a day after he was gone, nothing untoward happened. Only two people were replaced; the office secretary, a motherly sixty-year-old, was replaced by a perky young woman who, Jack thought, belonged in a TV commercial for kitchen cleanser, and the easy-going Information Technology Department supervisor who was replaced by George Price, an officious, tense man ten years younger than Jack.

Late Monday afternoon of the second week, Jack was summoned by Price, and cooled his heels while wasting thirty minutes in the man's sterile outer office listening to the steady, though faint, pounding of the office secretary's keyboard. Being summoned, not asked, and then made to wait was something he was unaccustomed to suffering, and it made him more than a tad cranky.

"Mr. Price will see you now, Mr. Wolfson," the new secretary, perky Miss Thompson, said.

"About time," he murmured, eliciting from Miss Thompson a small frown and narrowed eyes.

"Mr. Price is a busy man these days."

He grimaced at her officious tone, disliking her attitude as much as he did that of the new head of IT, a man who, if he stood next to Jack's six-three frame, would not rise above his shoulder. Price tried to make up for his lack of height with obnoxious, authoritarian bluster. Jack shrugged and stood up, not too quickly, and sauntered into the inner office.

Price did not get up from his chair, nor immediately look up from the desk where he was going through a file—a rather thin one—that Jack recognized as one belonging to Farnsworth and Company, an ongoing project in Lexington. It was resting on several other files, all of them rather skinny. Jack had spent considerable time undoing multiple errors in programming that IT specialists of various companies had made. He'd written little or nothing about what he had done.

"Jack, there are no progress reports on any of these projects. It's important I be kept abreast of how all these are coming along," Price said.

"I told Paul Anderson when he hired me that writing reports is not something I do."

"That right? Well, that's beside the point. If you are going to continue working here, you'll write reports. Do you understand?"

"I guess I do."

"Good. I'll want the Farnsworth updates on my desk tomorrow morning. I'd like the others done by the end of the week." Price picked up the phone and began dialing a number. He looked up at Jack who was standing looking down at him and frowned. "That's all, Jack."

"Indeed, it is," Jack said. "I quit."

George Price's face screwed into a look of disbelief then plummeted toward rage as he sputtered, "You can't just walk away from this job."

Jack walked away, feeling as he'd imagined Moses had when he threw down the golden calf his people worshipped in his absence.

Miss Thompson looked at him with worried eyes. "Can I help you with anything, Mr. Wolfson?"

"Just cut me a final check and mail it to me is all," he said, and donned his leather jacket, opened the front door and, unemployed, stepped into an icy blast. This February afternoon had sneaked in an infrequent weather pattern that swept through southern Tennessee, bringing snow, ice, and below-freezing temperatures.

The walk to his pickup truck was slippery; ice had already begun to form. His drive home on black ice was nerve-wracking and he passed three cars already in the ditch. Three sixteen-wheelers, giant trucks, were moving along as if the snow and ice were of no consequence. Those guys have the life, he thought, no bosses looking over their shoulders. He gave a sigh of relief as he turned into his drive and parked next to his wife's Camry.

Six months later, Jack wrestled a sixteen-wheeler onto Highway 31 and headed north toward Cincinnati, the stacked boxes of Jack Daniel's making the 400-horsepower engine growl with the weight. Almost a century before, around 1923, his great-great-grandfather would have been headed north as well, but with white lightning that had no federal excise tax sticker on it and with a lot less horsepower in his souped-up Model T Ford.

That same day he quit, remembering the sixteen-wheelers he'd admired on his way home in the storm, he'd gone on the internet and found an ad.

Tennessee Truck Driving School is so much more than just a truck driving school. Think of us as your personal gateway to a new career, a career in one of the largest industries in the country and one that is always in demand. We provide the truck driver training you need!

Signed up for a three-week course that guaranteed him a job on completion, he'd fallen in love with his monstrous rig the moment he crawled into its high seat. The only thing expected of him was that he shorten his hair and beard; his Moses/God demeanor did not quite fit the image of a long-hauler. Never having vowed to wear them long, he'd not felt compromised as he had when commanded to write reports, so he'd let the barber have a go at it. With the beard trimmed down to that of a sixteenth-century Tudor King, he no longer awed little ones at church.

No matter; he was King of the Road.

LOT'S WIFE

(17) *And it came to pass, when they had brought them forth abroad, that he said, escape for thy life; look not behind thee, neither stay thou in all the plain; escape to the mountain, lest thou be consumed.*

(24) Then the LORD rained upon Sodom and upon Gomorrah brimstone and fire from the LORD out of heaven; (25) And he overthrew those cities, and all the plain, and all the inhabitants of the cities, and that which grew upon the ground. (26) But his wife looked back from behind him, and she became a pillar of salt. ~**Genesis 19**

On Christmas Eve two months before my ninth birthday, Stanley Pankhurst and the rest of my future brother-in-law's family drove into my grandparents' farmyard in their gray 1940 Chevrolet. It was a raw, cold day and a dusting of snow lay on the ground, but I ran out in my shirtsleeves when I saw Stanley alighting from the car carrying several wrapped presents. He handed me one and from its firm heaviness, I knew it was a book. I loved books; almost as much as I loved salty food. The new present was wrapped in paper with multiple smiling Santa Clauses, elves, and reindeer peering from behind Christmas trees.

My mother had me place the present under the Christmas tree amid others with my name, all of which I had secretly squeezed and poked enough to know that all but one were necessities. My family believed in giving practical gifts, all that is but my Eberhart cousins, who gave one that was yet a mystery. But I loved books and could not wait to open the two presents I knew were not practical. After the Pankhursts had driven away, I sat on the sofa opposite the tree and stared with longing and anticipation.

Christmas morning finally arrived, and my mother and grandparents gathered in the sitting room around the tree. My uncle Burl, dressed in his fine, little Lord Fauntleroy finery stared down from his picture on the wall, looking saddened, I thought, for having missed Christmas for all the twenty-two years since he'd passed away with appendicitis.

My grandmother had made hot chocolate and coffee to drink while we settled onto "the good furniture" in front of a small, red native cedar my grandfather had chopped down and set in one corner of the room. Mother, grandmother, and I had festooned it with strings of popcorn and cranberries and a few precious ornaments. Having yet no electricity at the farm, there were no colored lights. My ample grandfather sat back comfortably and watched, enjoying my look of aggravation as my mother handed me one unwelcome "practical" gift package after another, my new shirts, winter gloves, and long underwear. I was very pleased with the pocket knife my cousins had given me but I was on the edge of my seat when she reached for the book. She teased when she finally picked up my last present and read aloud the name of my grandmother. I snatched at it as she handed it in the direction of my grandmother, but it disappeared behind my mother's back. Finally taking pity, she handed it over, and I ripped away the paper, letting Santa, reindeer, and elves fall in pieces to the floor.

My heart sank. The book title read:

Children's Bible Stories.

I don't know what I expected, maybe a book by Edgar Rice Burroughs or Felix Salten, my favorite authors at the time, but I certainly was not happy with Bible stories. I lay the book aside and taking my new knife to the coal bucket, whittled on a stick for a while before opening the book's cover. Though I would have preferred reading *Bambi* or a Tarzan book, I began reading, and even enjoying, many of the Bible stories. I disapproved highly of one of them, that of Sodom and Gomorrah. I didn't think too much of Lot; that he would leave his wife behind even if she was nothing but a piller of salt. And why was it so important to Him, the Lord Almighty, that she not look back and see what His wrath had wrought? Why turn her to salt? Being still of a somewhat literal mind-set, I wondered what happened to Lot's wife in the weeks and months that followed her punishment. Did that Old Testament God, who was a God of Wrath before Jesus came and changed things, see to it that she remained whole to warn others that they had better not disobey Him? Was she still sitting on a hill outside Sodom and Gomorrah? Wherever that was.

I ran these questions by my two cousins, Junior and Cecil, one of whom said "I bet you some farmer come along and made her into a salt lick for his cattle," and the other who opined that, "In my humble opinion, she got washed away in the next rainstorm."

I then asked my grandfather, who said, "Maybe some merchants took her and sold her for table salt." They had all looked serious and respectful of my questions, but left me in a worse dilemma than before I'd asked.

Striking a sulfur match to the kerosene cook stove in preparation for making dinner, my grandmother scowled at me when I told her of their notions. She always pulled her waist-length, silver-streaked hair into a severe bun atop her head, and to me she appeared perpetually angry even without the scowl. "Don't you believe everything those three tell you," she said. "Or you'll be a bigger fool than they are."

I didn't want to be a fool, much less a bigger one, but what they'd said seemed somewhat plausible to me. I was scared to contradict my grandmother, so did not mention that I was particularly worried about what my grandfather had said. His opinion made me wonder if pieces of Lot's wife might be in one of those boxes of Morton's salt.

It might be in the table salt I'd eaten or would eat in the future. Would it make me sick? When I was three, I'd become deathly ill from eating salt. My mother, father, ten-year-old sister, and I were staying in a cheap flat in Wichita Falls, Texas, where my father had found a job working as a salesman for the Jewel Tea Company. Asleep on the job, my sister, who was baby-sitting me, failed to see that I had found a box of salt left on the kitchen cabinet counter. For an hour or more, I spilled salt on the floor and licked great quantities of it. Afterward, I vomited for what seemed forever. Maybe it was some of Lot's wife in that salt that made me sick. I asked my cousin Bonnie Bell if she thought that was possible and she thought so, reminding me that the Good Book said that God moved in strange ways; so, what would be stranger than Lot's wife ending up in a box of salt?

I vowed then and there not to eat another grain of salt, just to be on the safe side but that night my grandmother served a pineapple-bedecked, salty Christmas ham for dinner. I sat crumbling cornbread into my milk, sculpting mountains in my mashed potatoes, and not looking at the meat. I'd helped salt that very ham after my grandfather butchered his hogs, and I knew how deliciously salty it was. I couldn't bring myself to taste it.

Seeing that I was not gorging myself on ham in my usual way, worry lines appeared at the corners my mother's soft brown eyes. Reaching across the oak table that had been set with my grandmother's best dishes, she interrupted my artistic potato mountain building to check my face for signs of a fever. "What is the matter with you? Are you feeling ill?"

"No. I just don't want to eat any salt. Lot's wife might be in it and I wouldn't want to eat any of her."

After she and my grandparents had finished laughing, my mother said, "Where did you get such a ridiculous idea?"

I glanced at my grandfather whose face had turned a bright red, either from laughing or embarrassment. "Grandpa told me," I said.

"And I told you not to believe everything him and those fool cousins of yours tell you," my grandmother said.

"Besides," my mother said, "Lot and his wife lived several thousand years ago. In a country far, far away over the ocean."

"But Bonnie Bell said the Good Book tells us that God moves in mysterious ways."

"Well, perhaps He does, but your grandpa was just fooling with you and there's no chance that grains of Lot's wife got into those pieces of ham. Now you eat some of that ham or I'm going to tan your hide. Such foolishness, I never heard the like."

I was more afraid of a hide tanning than I was of eating Lot's wife so I took a few bites of the ham.

I suffered no ill effects.

But for a good number of years after, I did wonder what happened to that pillar of salt every time I salted my food.

BIRD TALES

Starting when I was eight years old, my cousins Walter and Cecil Eberhart became my two favorite, male role models. I'd moved in with my grandparents Sherman who lived a good country half-mile from the Eberhart farm, so I saw them frequently. Everyone but me called Walter, "Junior," because he was named after my uncle Walter; and Cecil, "Hoot," because until he was well into his fourth year he said "hoot" when he tried to say "fruit." I called them, "Toughest," and "Next-to-the-Toughest" that summer because I couldn't keep their names and nicknames straight in my head. I've always had trouble remembering place names and given names. Toughest was twelve and Next-to-the-Toughest ten that summer and, when informing me about farm life or life in general, they treated me like Lucy did Charlie Brown in Charles "Sparky" Schulz's, *Peanuts* comic strip; always giving me "words of wisdom" that were erroneous, garbled, or outright falsehoods.

Junior, indeed the toughest of the two, was just growing into the handsome adolescent he would become and to me looking a lot like Errol Flynn whom I'd seen in *Dodge City* (1939) and *They Died with Their Boots On* (1941), this last movie coming out the summer I moved in with the Shermans. I was a little afraid of him because his practical jokes and roughhousing could sometimes be mean-spirited. Next-to-the-Toughest, Hoot, was more a Hoot Gibson sort, not all that handsome but living by the maxim, *Handsome is as Handsome Does*. From his rodeo fame and cowboy movies I'd become acquainted with Hoot Gibson (who could say fruit but was in some manner associated with hoot-owls, which is why they called him hoot) and, watching Cecil ride one of his father's yearling steers, I associated the two, both whom I admired. Hoot, in his role as older, wiser, and mostly beneficent cousin also had a very envious pair of ears that he could actually wiggle, something I was unable to do despite my long practices in front of a cracked mirror in my bedroom. Though only next to the toughest when put alongside Junior, Hoot was tough enough up against anyone his own age and came to my defense on several occasions when the older boys at our country school tried to bully me. Even though he was prone to giving me erroneous information and playing practical jokes at my expense, he was never mean-spirited like his brother. He was also more likely to include me in some of his escapades or projects; he let me help dig a hideout in the side of a mound of dirt, and let me carry water to pour down prairie dog burrows to force them out into the open where we could capture them in a gunnysack. It was easy for me to respect my Next-to-the-Toughest cousin's wisdom implicitly.

From these cousins and their sister, Bonnie Bell, I learned all the local superstitions, some of which lasted well into my adulthood. For instance, I learned to throw salt over my left shoulder whenever I spilled some; they told me it prevented the devil from seeing the possible bad luck that followed such an accident and taking some sort of advantage. This bit of folklore had likely been brought over by our European ancestors who believed they were throwing salt in the devil's eyes, thus ridding themselves of further evil or having him see any other sin they might commit. Both Junior and Cecil also warned that I should not look back to check if he was there or he might steal my soul. I neither wanted to lose my soul, nor did I want to take the chance, like Lot's wife I'd read about in a book of Bible stories, of looking back and ending up a pillar of salt, something I was sure both God and the devil had the power to transform me into.

Eight is an impressionable age, and things I was told I readily believed, particularly if they came from these two older cousins whom I idealized. So, when I took it into my head I wanted a pet meadowlark and told them so, they were quite interested in conveying their ideas.

Hoot immediately hatched the idea that we would most likely obtain such a treasure if we stole some of the birds' eggs from nests built in my grandfather Sherman's windbreak thicket, a band of stunted bushes and trees at the south end of his farm which had been planted to break the dust-laden Texas wind that came sweeping in from time to time. His idea was that we'd sneak them under an old setting hen who would hatch them and raise the chicks as her own. We gathered a dozen or so eggs, not all of them meadowlark eggs because in our excitement we decided any old egg would do. In a back corner of the hay barn we found a contrary Rhode Island Red hen setting on eight of her own eggs and, though she complained some and pecked at Hoot's hand when he reached to put our eggs under her, we left quite satisfied that she would do her job. Didn't happen. Those bird eggs we put so much hope in were too delicate and they all broke the first day we placed them. On discovering this, Hoot wiggled his ears at me and waxing philosophical said, "I guess you just can't trust those old hens to be a good mama to meadowlark eggs." That year there were fewer meadowlarks in the pasture to sing for me.

Junior then said he'd heard that if you could throw salt on a bird's tail, you could easily capture it and put it in a cage till it was tamed. I spent hours stalking birds to throw a handful of salt on their tails. I very much wanted a pet meadowlark; I loved their happy calls on summer days.

Years later I read a Swedish fairy tale by Anna Walenburg that clued me in on how they might have come on the idea. The story was about a fatherless young boy whose mother was very poor. He was always wishing for things—a bike, a sled, even a cheap clasp knife. An old man who overheard him wishing for things told the boy that if he could sprinkle salt on a magpie's tail, the bird would grant him anything he desired. Like me, the boy could not get close to one no matter how hard he tried. But one rather clever, though, greedy, magpie said to the boy, "Bring me something of value and in return I'll sit still long enough for you to sprinkle salt on my tail." But everything the boy labored hard to buy and bring was not good enough, and he was sent back time and again to labor more. As years passed the boy, turned man, accumulated great wealth and eventually brought a great deal of money to the bird who then allowed the salt to be sprinkled and three wishes granted. But when the man tried to think of what he would wish for, he could think of nothing; he now had it all.

The meadowlarks I stalked did not speak to me nor demand anything of me. They all flew away well before I came near. But at the time I had great faith in my cousin's wisdom and would have spent much more time pursuing the birds had not my grandmother Sherman discovered I'd taken her box of salt and demanded I tell her what I'd done with it. I was quick to tell her of my efforts to catch a bird by throwing salt on its tail.

"Where in the world did you get that notion?" she asked.

"Junior and Hoot said so."

"Those boys are just making a fool out of you. They know you can never get close enough to a bird to throw salt on its tail. I thought you had more common sense than that," she said, her face taking on that harsh, granite stiffness it assumed when she was displeased with my grandfather, which was most of the time. She didn't think he had that much common sense either.

I was mortified to think I was in the same boat as my grandfather, so I gave up my quest for a pet bird and settled on a tarantula I captured in a fruit jar.

I did wonder where my cousins came by their idea of catching a bird by salting its tail until I discovered that Swedish fairy tale which taught the wisdom of hard work and that diligence would bring to one everything that was wished for; that magic is not necessary to attain one's goals. But my cousins were not familiar with the tale, and so were not trying to teach me diligence. What they did teach me, though, was not to believe every fanciful story the older and supposedly wiser are sometimes all too willing to tell.

SMALL TOWN GUY

From out of somewhere deep in slumber, Sam Holcomb tripped through jumbled images of singing and dancing children and their beautiful mother, climbed from sleep, and fumbled for the phone on his bedside table. Jungle drums pounded in his temples. His first thought was that his mother was calling. But it was not his mother. Virginia Josephs answered his hello. She had been the one who wandered through his troubled dreams. Hearing her voice made the drums' cadence quicken.

The night before, Sam had made himself sloppy drunk for the first time in his life, and was sure he'd made an absolute fool of himself. Dr. Leo Weiss had plied him with martinis, as foul a concoction as Sam had ever tasted, and he'd drank them down—and become a sloppy drunk. Now Weiss would decide in the next couple of days whether to accept a sloppy drunk into his residency program at the St. Louis Regional Hospital. Sam should have told Weiss he was a Baptist and didn't drink, but he'd wanted to make a good impression, show he was worldly wise and sophisticated, not just a small-town guy.

Worse, Weiss's beautiful, married daughter, Virginia Josephs, and her two children were visiting her parents and must have thought him a country bumpkin and a bore. He'd really wanted to impress her and her parents. Likely as not, she had laughed along with them about this weird person showing up for pediatric training.

It had been 12:00 A.M. by the time he stumbled up the steps to his rented room after dinner and staggered to bed, falling in clothes and all. He'd not awakened until ten o'clock, with just enough time to make it to an appointment with still another member of the department who had brow-beat him with questions about muscular dystrophy, a disease of which the man was considered an outstanding expert. Sam had felt bruised. Back at his apartment he'd loosened his tie and dropped onto the bed barely closing his eyes before the phone rang.

"Did you survive the interview this morning?" Virginia Josephs asked.

Jolted by her having called him, he was at a loss for words but managed to croak, "I'm not sure." Her soft laughter made his throat muscle tighten even more.

"I felt like he turned me inside out. Everything was showing." His words sounded hoarse and raspy

"Wonderful. My dad told me that's what he likes to do. Makes him feel as though he gets a better idea of what a potential resident is like. I'll bet he liked you."

"I just hope he didn't find out too much of what he didn't like." Not knowing why she was calling him, he asked, "Did your dad ask you to call?"

"I'm not part of the evaluation team, Sam. No reporting to the authorities."

"Oh."

"I just wondered if you were busy this evening. I'd like you to go to the ballet with me. Mother and Dad can't go and I have their tickets. Actually, Dad suggested I ask you since my husband couldn't take me. He thought you ought to see the cultural advantages St. Louis offers."

Sam wanted to say yes, to have the opportunity to be with Virginia for the evening. But the idea of going into public with a married woman was something he couldn't imagine. "I'd like to go, Virginia, but I don't know anything about ballet."

"You don't have to know anything about it." She laughed again. "You just watch it."

In a novel he'd read and a couple of movies he'd seen, everyone wore tuxedos to a ballet and took their lady to dinner after the performance. He had no clothes other than the one suit he'd worn last night. He didn't even have enough money to invite her to dinner. "I don't have a tuxedo."

"You wore a very nice suit last night."

"I thought you had to wear a tux."

"You'll be fine. You'll have a great time."

"I really can't afford to take you out to a restaurant afterward." A rush of shame almost completely choked off his words. He couldn't remember feeling so penniless since he'd admitted to his first-year college English professor that he hadn't enough money to pay for someone to type his term paper. After his performance of the evening before he was now sure that she would think him a complete dunce.

"Sam. This is not a big deal. We're just going to the ballet. No frills. Just thrills. You'll love it. And I'm eating with my kids before we go, so I hope you'll have something beforehand, too. Okay?"

"What time do I pick you up?"

"Don't bother to come to pick me up. I'll drive by your place at seven. Curtain time is at eight. Bye for now." She hung up before

Sam could even say goodbye, or think of something else to excuse his not going.

Ballet, thought Sam. I'll feel as out of place as a clown in a church choir. Or a sinner at a Sunday School social. Sam pictured Virginia's young daughter twirling about on her toes the evening before, wobbling uncertainly as she performed for him. He'd rather have her entertain him than go to a performance by skimpily dressed women cavorting across a stage, or some muscular man throwing himself into the air, prancing about on his toes.

His mother would scold him; she didn't allow dancing into her or his life. To dance or even watch dancing was to let sin enter in and steal one's soul. To do so with a woman who was still married was unthinkable. Maybe they were right, that he was starting down a road so steep he was in danger of speeding into the pit.

Sam paced the sidewalk in front of the apartment building, fretting more with each minute that ticked past seven, imagining Virginia changing her mind or having to stay with one of the children, sick with a sudden outbreak of chickenpox or measles. He heard a phone ringing somewhere nearby and thought for certain it was her, trying her best to let him know she wouldn't be there. At ten past seven, when he saw her drive up in a fancy new BMW, he became obsessed with another kind of uncertainty. Why had he accepted her invitation? Did Weiss really ask her to invite him to the ballet? If he didn't, and found out, would that be the end of Sam's hopes for a residency. Without the residency would he be denied the chance of working with Weiss? Was he letting his future take a dangerous ride in the front seat of this luxury car parked at curbside?

Virginia rolled down her window and gave him a guilty little wave. "Sorry I'm late. I hope you didn't think I'd forgotten. At the last minute that son of mine took it into his head that I shouldn't leave.

He threw a fit." She spoke rapidly, as if she had to get everything out in one breath. Her hair had more shine and her lips were fuller. She'd done something to her eyes that made them turn up at the corners like a sultry gypsy. She wore a velvet dress that seemed to flow about her when she moved. "I'm so glad you decided to come with me. I think you'll love the ballet they're performing tonight. It's *Swan Lake*."

"I knew you'd be here. I never had a moment's doubt." Sam let himself into the car that smelled of new leather and factory oils. He sank into a plush seat and was relieved he had not insisted on picking her up in the Chevy beater he'd driven up from Texas.

Virginia gave a sideways glance. "Friendship is built on trust, Doctor." She pulled the car away from the curb and accelerated onto the main street; the engine hummed quietly.

"You're right. Truth is, I wore a hole in that poor woman's front walk. I imagined every possible reason you wouldn't show up."

"That's more like it."

"Can I expect the truth too?" There were a number of things he would like to have clear, but he feared the questions he'd ask would sound sophomoric, naïve, or even moralistic. Was she inviting him for other reasons than to show him the cultural side of St. Louis?

Virginia kept her eyes on the road for a moment and then nodded. "You can, though I have to admit that sometimes I don't know what the truth about me is."

"Did your dad actually ask you to take me to the ballet tonight?"

"I guess I volunteered."

"Why?"

"Ask me a hard question."

"If the question is easy for you, go ahead." When she was silent, he added. "Actually, I'd like to know why I'm doing it."

"Now that's an impossible question for me. No one can answer it but you. But as for the easier one, I'm doing this partly because even though you were almost falling down drunk, you paid more attention and were much nicer to me during those three hours last night than my husband has been in years."

"I'm sorry to hear that, Virginia. I mean about your husband." Sam, more uneasy now, did not know what else to say. This wasn't right, but he could not bring himself to ask her to turn around and take him back to his apartment. "You said it was only part of the reason."

"You spent more time with my kids in an hour than my husband has in six months. Melissa and Larry fell in love with you. Melissa has decided that she wants you to come to her recital next week and Larry keeps asking when he can see Uncle Sam."

Sam laughed. "Remember those enlistment posters during the Second World War saying, **Uncle Sam Needs You**? When my mother named me, she never stopped to think that I might be an Uncle Sam someday."

Virginia took a deep breath and went on. "Larry wants you to visit again so the two of you can play and sing together." She began to breathe fast and was teary as she turned to look at Sam. "So why are you here? Remember, we're being honest with each other."

The first thing that came to his mind was his college girlfriend, Joanie; how long it had been since he'd held her in his arms. Those few months with Joanie had been close, but then when he entered medical school, they'd drifted apart. "I haven't had any honest warmth from a woman in a long time."

"No wife? No girlfriend?"

"I've been too busy."

"Aren't you ever lonely?"

"I am lonely." Sam did not want to face that fact but it was true. "And last night you were really kind. You made me feel included. I wasn't lonely for a while."

"So, it wasn't just my good looks then?"

"We're being honest here? Yes. It was partly your good looks. I had a hard time keeping my eyes off you."

"I noticed. It was flattering."

"I was afraid you'd think me rude. That your mother and father would too."

"I can't vouch for them. Only me."

"I don't think your mother liked me very much. I couldn't tell about your dad."

"My mother is very protective of her family. It's too bad I showed such an interest in you. I think she didn't like that, not you."

"How about your dad?"

"My dad liked you. And even if he hadn't, you have nothing to worry about. They really need another decent resident to fill in next year's quota. Dad thinks you fill the bill."

"He wasn't a little suspicious about your volunteering to escort me tonight?"

"To tell you the truth, which I guess is our ground-rule, I think he's secretly championing me. He can't stand Richard."

"And your mother?"

"Of course, she didn't like the idea, but my father overrode her objections. She'll have your neck in a noose if we don't behave, and you don't get me home on time. She's pretty strict."

Virginia pulled into the indoor parking at the theater, and sat for a moment as if in in thought.

"Won't some of your acquaintances be here this evening?" Sam asked. "They'll talk."

"I think I'm past caring. But, no, they won't talk. If they caught us smooching in the back seat of this car or driving into a motel they might. Remember, you're a prospective member of the elite academic community, and I'm showing you one of the cultural benefits of living in our fair city, convincing you to come here for your pediatric residency. My lawyer husband is working on an important case and couldn't join us."

"That wouldn't pass muster in Vernon, Texas. If you spent more than five seconds in public with someone other than your husband, the local tongue-waggers would have the news all over town. Your reputation would be ruined,"

"What about yours?"

"In Texas, women's reputations tarnish easier than men's."

"Quaint. Do you still want to go to the ballet and ruin my reputation in Texas?"

"My daddy used to say, 'In for a penny, in for a dime.'"

"Meaning what?"

"That we've got this far so let's not back out now."

She took his arm as they crossed the street, smiling up at him, teasing. "I hope there aren't any Texans around."

Just before the doors to the auditorium closed, they walked through the empty foyer into the darkening hall and found their seats near the front as the curtain began to rise. Sam, his back stiff, felt as if all eyes in the theater were focused on them. Despite his bravado with Virginia, he was uneasy here among people who might know her. Or her husband. He settled into his seat and Virginia slipped in beside him, tossed her head, sending her hair back from her face, then smoothed it back to one side, revealing to Sam the lovely curve of her neck, glowing softly in the footlights. Upon the stage one lone, collapsed figure unfolded arms and legs, opening like a flower, and began to dance.

Two-and-a-half hours later Virginia pulled to a stop in front of a seedy-looking bar not far from the Wash U campus. Young men and women, most arm in arm, entered an open door from out of which came the buzz of voices mixed with the driving beat of drums and guitar.

"This is a place I loved when I was at Wash U. Cheap beer and sandwiches big enough for two. My treat." Virginia led him into the smoky bar, a railroad-car-sized seating area with booths along both walls and, bunched together in the center, tables where young men and women ambled about or sat shoulder to shoulder in animated conversation over their beers. Virginia squirmed through the small space, no wider than a deer path in the forest, left open for the pitcher-bearing waitstaff prowling for empties. She grabbed the only two empty chairs left and squeezed them together at a table where two others had gained a purchase and were deeply into each other's embrace. They didn't look up. "This will have to do," Virginia said. She signaled to a passing waiter, pointing to a pitcher on a nearby table.

He shook his head, pointed to a glass, and held up two fingers and shouted "We don't want a repeat of last night, do we?"

"Actually, dad and I thought you were lots of fun. You loosened up and enjoyed yourself with a little encouragement from alcohol," she shouted back.

"Seems as if tonight I've loosened up a bit too much—and without the alcohol. No telling what I'd do with a few beers in me."

She arched an eyebrow at him, smiled and said something he could not hear above the general racket of music, loud talking, and hysterical laughing from a woman two tables away.

"How do we hear each other?" Sam yelled above the general babble.

"The trick is to sit close," Virginia moved nearer, her knee and thigh pressed against Sam as she turned to face him.

So close now that he could feel her breath on his cheek, Sam had to check an impulse to kiss her. "Promotes togetherness?"

"Promotes hearing." She glanced at the couple sitting at the table with them. They were in a deep embrace. "And perhaps other things as well." She moved her lips closer, tilted her head slightly, and with her warm fingers touched his cheek.

Sam's eyes widened and his muscles tensed. He hadn't expected this and was at a loss for words.

"I'm sorry," she said and pulled away, her face reddening.

"Don't say that. I didn't mean to hurt your feelings. It's just that you surprised me."

"I'm sorry," she said again.

Sam took her hand in his and squeezed. "I'm the one that's sorry." Her hands felt so soft that he did not want to let go. And he wanted to recapture the moment he'd lost when she raised her lips to him.

She started to pull her hand away, but he held on tighter and gazed at her, and it seemed that, like an empty cistern after a long drought, he became filled to the brim with a cloudburst of longing. He really wanted her but had to fight to keep the voices of his mother and pastor at bay. "I don't want you to get hurt," he said.

"I'm already hurting," she said, tears welling in her eyes.

Sam pulled her closer and touched his lips to hers, but she put her hand behind his head and kissed him deeply before pulling away

"Have I started something you could be sorry for if we don't stop now?"

"In for a penny . . ."

"In for a dime?"

"Will you go back to the apartment with me?" Sam asked.

"Do you really think we ought to bet the whole dime?"

Still, he almost choked when he said, "I'm already in."

"I didn't think the boys down south moved ahead this fast."

Sam colored, sure the area around the table actually lit up by the embarrassed glow from his cheeks. "I've not really been with anyone for a long time. I don't know what to do. How to act."

Virginia laughed. "Been-with sounds so quaint, so—so biblical."

Sam's face fell. "I guess I grew up in a quaint biblical place."

"Oh, Sam, I'm sorry. I love the way you are." Taking his hand in both of hers she squeezed hard. "Let's go." She rose and led him back through the crowd to the car and they drove in silence to his apartment. Parking in front, she turned off the motor, leaned forward and kissed him on the lips. "I'm in for the whole dime," she said.

He could almost hear Pastor Simmons's deep voice scolding from the pulpit. The image of her little daughter's angelic face came into his mind. His mother's disapproving glare followed. He pulled away and sat facing forward. "I can't do this, Virginia. I just can't. Not tonight."

Virginia's eyes widened and tears ran down her face. "I'm sorry." She turned away from him and dabbed at her eyes.

"Virginia, please. I'm just confused."

Turning to him, she took his hand and hugged it to her cheek.

"Please call me," she said, drew him close and kissed him once more and then pushed him toward the car door.

Sam's body ached as he climbed out onto the sidewalk. Tears of frustration spilled down his cheek as he watched her drive away. A melancholy descended on him as he thought of how he'd denied something he might never have a chance at again. But how could he have actually pursued a married woman any further?

The stairs to his apartment stretched upward forever, his legs like lead weights holding him back from ever reaching the top.

SNAKES

Genesis 3

14 So the LORD god said to the serpent, "Cursed are you above all the livestock and all the wild animals! Because you have done this, You will crawl on your belly and you will eat dust all the days of your life.

15 And I will put enmity between you and the woman, and between your offspring and hers; he will crush your head, and you will strike his heel."

The snake did not fare well in the Garden of Eden where the Judeo-Christian God of the Old Testament cursed it. In Western Culture he has always suffered the reputation of being an evil force, though in others he has assumed the role of everything from a god to the Egyptians, who kept cobras as pets, to a valued totem animal for the Parintintin Indians of Brazil.

All future Parintintin shamans in the Amazon jungle are chosen by an older practitioner who, after picking an acolyte while the infant is still within its mother's womb, dreams a totem animal into him. It is not uncommon for that animal to be a snake. Thereafter, the child's strength and power are channeled through this totem.

Though not dreamed for me by a shaman, I could very well claim the snake as my totem; for I acquired the mark of the snake, a half-dollar sized, brown nevus on my shoulder, while still in my mother's womb, and I carried it for seventy-five years. Perhaps that totem saved me from ever having to join the White Fang Club, whose members have survived a rattlesnake bite on the hunts that took place near my home in Okeene, Oklahoma, during the annual rattlesnake roundup. On the many hunts I attended and despite the many rattlesnakes I handled, I was never bitten. Could I have been protected by the power of my snake totem? I really don't believe so. I was always very careful. It was through some carelessness on my superstitious mother's part, however, that the fanciful idea came about that a snake was responsible for my birthmark.

Soon after she became pregnant with me, when she was twenty-four years old, my father had taken off for parts unknown; he was a rather wild young man, and while he was absent, my mother was staying with her parents on Dixon Heights, a rather grand name for the rather humble farmhouse that rested on the only rise of ground within ten miles in any direction of Hobart, Oklahoma. It was while she gathered eggs in the Dixon Heights henhouse that I supposedly acquired my mark.

She described entering the henhouse, a small shed that, during the night and on stormy days, provided shelter for the fifty laying hens my grandparents kept. Inside, it was heavy with the thick smell of old hay in the nests, of the birds' oily feathers, their store-bought crushed grain, and fresh droppings. One wall was covered from floor to ceiling with hens' nests where once a day the eggs were taken, sometimes to be plucked from under mean-eyed sitting hens that pecked at invading hands. On a hot summer day while she was gathering eggs, my mother reached up into a nest that was above eye level, and took hold of a black snake that had sneaked in to steal eggs. "I fainted dead away," she explained many times during my early years. "And that's why you have that birthmark on your shoulder," she claimed, always with great conviction.

Through my life there were many times when I handled snakes, taking one to a college class to give a demonstration speech on how to milk venom from its jaws, capturing and selling them at the local rattlesnake roundup where they were used for medical experiments or butchered and fried to sell to spectators at the roundup, and pushing them aside with a stick when they blocked the desert paths on which I hiked with my wife and/or relatives who were too terrified to come within twenty feet of the reptile.

My last encounter with a snake was with an anaconda while vacationing in the Brazilian Amazon and visiting a native settlement on a tributary of the Rio Negro river. An Indian man had caught the ten-foot snake in his fishing net and held it captive to intrigue the tourists. Not afraid of snakes, I took the animal into my hands and wrapped it around my neck as two young female lawyers looked on with alarm. The snake wound around my arm and turned its head to gaze at me with its dark-hooded eyes. My wife, Carolyn, then took it from me with no fear whatsoever. I then persuaded the two young lawyers to do the same, suggesting that when they returned to practice, they could boast to their colleagues. Pictures were taken and admired later as we all sat around a table eating piranha stew and listening to a Brazilian myth, about snakes not unlike that of the biblical Garden of Eden.

In one of the Brazilian Parintintin cultures it was told that an old woman went into the woods to gather nuts. While eating small, white berries there, she accidentally ingested a snake's egg and, later, again while in the forests, gave birth to a snake. The snake climbed a Brazil nut tree and magically broke open the hard, outer cover of the nuts, raining many seeds down upon the old lady. She gathered them into her basket and took them back to the village, but not before the snake once more entered her. When she returned to the village, her sons asked how she was able to crack the hard, outer shells to get to such a copious number of Brazil nuts and she told them of the snake. She then conspired with her sons to kill the snake when she again went into the forest to the tree, instructing them to cut it exactly in two. Once there, the snake again emerged from her, climbed the tree and magically broke the hard shells, raining Brazil nuts down upon the old lady. But as it descended the tree, to reenter the old woman, her sons rushed out of hiding and cut it squarely in two. The snake died clinging to the tree and became the vine that now covers many of the trees.

The mother immediately died. As she had instructed them at some former time, they burned her on a funeral pyre and scattered her ashes over a parcel of barren land. Weeks later they returned to pay homage, and found that the land was abundant with all manner of wonderful things to eat. They did not know what to call these foods but a woodpecker flew over and, calling out, gave the brothers names for the foods and knowledge of how to prepare corn beer and how to remove the poison from manioc so it can be safely eaten.

The snake of Western mythology tempts the woman to eat fruit from the tree of knowledge, which causes her and Adam to be banished from paradise. The snake of Brazilian Indians, repeatedly born out of the woman, rains nuts down upon her and, at its death, is responsible for the death of the old woman. But this results in the sons gaining knowledge and entering into a paradise garden. As far as I know, the snake that scared my mother had no power for good or for evil, other than supposedly supplying me with the birthmark about which I always felt selfconscious when undressed in a gym locker. Unless, that is, the connection being that my mother was deathly afraid of doctors and well as snakes. She told me that when I went off to college, I should choose any profession other than that of medicine. Perhaps it is ironic that it was that very same profession I chose and perhaps even more so that a part of the ancient symbol of that profession is—yes, you guessed it if you didn't already know—a snake. (The caduceus is often mistakenly used as a symbol of medicine and medical practice [especially in North America], due to historical confusion with the traditional medical symbol, the rod of Asclepius. The Rod of Asclepius has only a single snake and no wings, so is similar in form to the caduceus with its two snakes. Historically, the caduceus was the magic staff of Hermes [Mercury], the god of commerce, eloquence, invention, travel, and theft. I suppose there are some who today might think the medical profession in the hands of corporations is in danger of becoming more of a commercial enterprise in the hands of thieves than a care-giving organization.)

The more common medical symbol used outside the United States derives from ancient Greek mythology. According to the Greeks, the mythical figure Aesculapius discovered medicine by watching as a snake used herbs to bring another snake back to life. I don't think that either the rod of Aesculapius or the caduceus symbols were what induced me to go into training to be a physician, but it does seem appropriate that one who is said by his mother to have been marked by the snake should have such an emblem demonstrating his profession. And were I as superstitious as my mother was, I could believe that the mark allowed snakes to recognize that they are my totem animal and therefore I was deserving of protection from their bite. But what if I were to no longer have such a mark? If I handled snakes without it, would I be as protected? At age seventy-five, I was able to test that idea.

At that advanced age it became necessary for a dermatologist to remove my birthmark; it had spawned a basal cell carcinoma. I'd known that was a possibility since medical school. Now I sport only a thin scar but, though minus my mark of the serpent, I've felt no need for extra vigilance when tramping through the rattlesnake-infested Superstition Mountains as I do every year around the end of February or first of March. I have yet to be bitten by my totem animal.

Any superstitions I might have once had grew frail and long ago died.

GROWING SNAKES

There were those in my early years who filled my head with superstitious snake lore. My grandparents, Granny and Pa Wilkerson, lived in a two-room shanty that sat on sixty acres from which Pa scratch-farmed about as much flint rock for his fences as he did corn for his family and the hogs. While living with them on their unnamed farm near Gentry, Arkansas, Pa told me that if I dropped a horsetail hair into the water-well, the hair would turn into a snake. Being a curious sort, I hurried to the barnyard to collect a few hands full of hair that tended to catch on splits in the wooden fence posts at which Old Tony, a large dun workhorse, and Trixie, the mare, stood switching flies away with their tails. But when I announced my intention to drop the first ones down the well, Pa said, "I don't think your Ma or Granny will be very happy if they draw up a bucket of drinking water and find it full of snakes."

That put a kink in my plans because I knew I'd be in big trouble especially with my mother's terror of snakes. Things would have stopped there, but I told my uncle Keith about how disappointed I was.

Keith, being an understanding sort, assured me that I could still have my hair-born snakes. "You just have to leave them overnight in a Mason jar filled with well water and you'll have snakes by morning."

Having found a more acceptable approach to growing snakes, I borrowed a quart mason jar from my granny, filled it with well water. When that didn't work, at the advice of Uncle Keith, I tried spring water. Then I used water from the rain-barrel. Failing to grow snakes in rain-barrel water, my Aunt Charlene suggested that I try using a few drops of fresh milk. Milk or water, the results were the same: no snakes.

This rather far-fetched idea of the birth of snakes was shared by others than my Wilkerson family. As far back as May 16, 1887, the *New York Times* quoted a *Toronto Mail's* article in which Dr. George D. Griffin, of Parkdale, Ontario, wrote: "The 'horse-hair' question can be answered in this way. The roots of the hair must be with it or it will not become a 'living snakelike' existence. In muddy, tepid water it, through the roots, in accordance with the law of life by the law of affinity, absorbs vitalizing elements the same as it did when on the animal. And substances of the hair being animal life as well as vegetable, it is naturally more or less sensitive to touch. I have seen the horse-hair phenomenon, and I once saw it duplicated a thousand-fold in a stagnant pool where the hair of a slaughtered hog had been thrown, and in handfuls as pulled out by the roots they exhibited the same kind of life, but more active than the horse-hair does..."

Years later I learned that "horsehair snakes" are parasitic worms that look so much like hairs from a horse's mane or tail that one might think them horsehairs come to life. These organisms mature in the abdomen of grasshoppers and crickets and are completely harmless to humans. The mysterious creatures somehow manage to induce the grasshopper to jump in a stream or pool of water where it dies and the worms swim out into the water to seek mates. They are sometimes referred to by the name Gordian Worm for their habit of curling into a twisted ball resembling the knot that Alexander the Great severed with his sword when failing the task of untying it. I don't think any of my family knew about either Alexander the Great, or Dr. George D. Griffin, of Parkdale, Ontario. The tale must have blown down with a north wind from Canada all the way to Gentry, Arkansas. I don't know if my grandfather truly believed in the horsetail hair snakes or if he might have been steering my interest in them to guide me away from an interest in those dangerous ones that did inhabit his land. He needn't have bothered; had I come across a timber rattler or a water moccasin I would have had the sense not to handle it. More sense than I had for believing horsehairs could be induced to grow snakes.

BEHEADING A SNAKE

When I was eight, my mother and I went to live with her parents on a farm ten miles from Hobart, Oklahoma. We lived only a half mile from my cousin Bonnie Bell and her two older brothers who filled me in on all the local snake folklore in that vast land of cotton fields, pastures, windbreak thickets, and cattle ponds. There are forty-six species of snakes living in Oklahoma, but I only knew about black snakes and the ones my cousins assured me were quite dangerous. There was the hoop snake that could curl into a loop and roll down a hill after you. There was the milk snake that could suck the milk right out of the Jersey cow my grandfather owned, and leave us without butter or cream. There were puff adders that could breathe out a poison that could kill a person twenty-five feet away and a snake that could spit venom into a person's eyes and blind him. Of course, none of this was true but I didn't know it.

There were water moccasins in the pond, however, and rattlesnakes in the mountains six miles away, but a lot more harmless garter, black, and king snakes wriggled through the grasses in the pasture. The regularity with which people kill a snake first and ask questions later might lead one to believe that the world is overrun with venomous serpents. In fact, the poisonous ones only make up about 10 percent of snake species worldwide. The rest are harmless and even necessary in keeping down the rat, mouse, and rabbit populations as well as other animals that are pests to farmers. But, according to my uncle Walter Eberhart, there were no beneficial snakes in the world and they all needed killing. On seeing one, he always did just that.

On a hot August afternoon, I watched the approach of a red dust-cloud spilling from behind my uncle Walter's green Ford truck. He had come by to pick my mother and me up and drive us to the cotton field where we were to chop cotton, so he braked to a stop, and let the dust spill on down the road as he waited for us to climb aboard. In the front seat, I could see Bonnie Bell waving to us. My older cousins, Junior and Hoot, leaned over the cab of the truck, letting the breeze curl and snap their hair into a dark fan that whipped at their faces. A group of townspeople, hired for the day to chop cotton, sat or stood in the back of the truck bed. I ran toward the truck, but stopped when Walter yelled, "Snake. Watch out!"

My mother grabbed my arm, pulling me away from the snake which had coiled fifteen feet away. She was deathly afraid of snakes and no distance away was far enough.

Junior and Hoot spilled out of the back, leaving the others to peer over the edges of the sideboards. Picking up a tree branch lying under the mulberry trees that lined the front of my grandpa's house, Hoot demanded, "Let me tend to that snake."

"You boys leave that snake to me." Walter waved them away. His oil-stained overalls bagged around his skinny butt, and he wore a felt

BEHEADING A SNAKE

hat with the brim turned down in front and the sweatband black with sweat and dust. A corncob pipe was clamped firmly in his mouth as if he were afraid it would get away.

Hoot reached with the dry tree limb and poked at the snake's coils making it hiss and then slither toward the ditch so quickly I was sure it would get away.

One of the women left standing in the truck bed held her skirt up from her ankles as if afraid that a snake could easily climb up the side of the truck and shinny up her skirt.

Before the snake escaped, Walter reached down, grabbed it by the tail, and began to swing it gently back and forth. "You do this, boys, and it can't crawl up its body and bite you."

My mother screamed and tried to drag me further away but I broke free, leaving her to run to the front porch where, pushing her sun bonnet back so her face was framed like one of the oval pictures hanging on the walls of my grandparents' home, screamed at me, "Clifton, you get up to this porch right now!"

Knowing she wouldn't dare leave the porch to come after me, I ignored her as Walter continued to swing the snake and address us, "Now pay close attention and I'll show you-all something here. In just a minute I'm going to snap this snake like I would a bullwhip. Anybody know what's going to happen then?"

When no one responded he asked again, "Anybody know?" Behind wire-rim glasses Walter squinted his eyes against the brightness of the early morning sun. "Well, now, cat got all your tongues?"

"You're going to make that snake madder'n a wet hen," Bonnie Bell piped up from the inside the truck cab where she had remained seated and staring out the window. "That's what you're a-gonna do."

"You hush up, now." Walter shook his head at her, his dark eyes following as she climbed down from the truck and stalked some distance away and sat down with her back against a crooked fencepost.

"No siree. I'm going to snap its head right off its body. My daddy learnt that trick down in Texas back in nineteen-six when he was helping drive cattle up into Indian Territory. Only difference, he was using full-growed rattlers."

"Why don't you just kill that thing?" My mother yelled. "Clifton, you mind me now. Come over here this second."

I darted in closer to uncle Walter, convinced she wouldn't come within a hundred feet while I stood so close to that black snake.

My grandfather Sherman, joining the crowd of people, adjusted the shoulder strap of his overalls and then crossed his arms. "Not likely, Walter, that your pa ever snapped a rattlesnake's head off. He'd a shot it with his pistol."

"Well, now, this was probably when you didn't know him that well, Jim." Uncle Walter took his pipe out of his mouth and held it in one hand while with the other he began to swing the snake in larger circles, faster and faster until it became a black haze. "You just watch me, folks, and you be the judge of what my daddy taught me." He jerked the snake to a halt in midair, snapping it like a whip.

I didn't hear the cracking of a bullwhip but I did see something black sail through the air and land twenty-feet away. Everybody's eye followed its flight. Mother stood open-mouthed as I charged after my cousin, Hoot, leaving Walter standing with a smug look on his face, the snake dangling limp from his hand.

"Lord a mercy, Dad," yelled Cecil. "That weren't no head. It's a baby rabbit."

On the ground I could see the slick and blackened form of a baby rabbit, swallowed whole, its ears still pressed against its head. I jumped when Walter gave out a loud yelp and let the snake, its mouth inches from the hand that held it, drop to the ground.

Grandfather laughed and the town folks who had climbed down to watch scattered as the snake crawled toward them. One little girl

BEHEADING A SNAKE

screamed and swung herself up onto the truck bed. Bonnie Bell jumped and ran to the house where she stood with my mother on the porch, shading her eyes as she yelled for her daddy to catch the snake. Uncle Walter raced after it and took hold of the slithery tail just before the snake disappeared under the truck.

"Guess I'm just a little out of practice, folks. Let's give this another try." He set the pipe on the truck's running board, ashes and wasted shreds spilling onto the worn metal, a thin stream of smoke rising up from them. Twice more he twirled the snake snapping it like a whip and each time something black flew through the air, shouts went up from the townspeople and each time Hoot yelled, "It's another 'un."

Grandfather hollered, "How many baby rabbits you going to pop out of that poor old snake, Walter, before you give up?"

One of the women in the truck lost her breakfast over the side at that moment and all eyes turned to her. Blushing, she sat down so only the top of her head showed above the sides of the truck bed.

"Well, well, well," Walter said, shaking his head. "I never saw the like of this before. Except at a friend of mine's house once. He owned a boa constrictor. That critter swallowed a goat, hooves and all. And I hear tell of snakes in South America that are big enough to swallow a man."

Hoot and his brother, Junior, walked dispiritedly back and climbed into the truck. The men who had come to work and who had stood around smoking cigarettes while watching uncle Walter, and waiting to get in the field climbed in after my cousins.

Walter tossed the snake into the weed-choked ditch where it lay, dead or senseless. Reaching down, he grabbed his pipe and sucked hard, as if to bring back to life what dead embers still lingered in the bowl, then swung himself up onto the running board and into the cab, "We're a wasting time. Everybody get aboard."

Bonnie Bell and I climbed into the truck bed, and wriggled in between Hoot and Junior who, as we rode to the field, told us again about the coachwhip snake that was so fast it could, quick as a wink, chase me down, wrap me up in its coils, whip me to death with its tail, and then make sure I was dead by sticking its tail up my nose to see if I was still breathing. After the scene with Uncle Walter I only half listened. Bonnie Bell just rolled her eyes.

That evening, when I got back home from chopping cotton, I approached the ditch with a great deal of caution but found no snake, dead or alive; it had been eaten or else regained consciousness and slithered away. I wasn't frightened of finding the poor old black snake and not even nervous that I might come upon a coachwhip snake. Truth be known, I lost a bit of faith that day in believing the claims that some cousins and adult relatives made about their knowledge, powers, or skill.

CAT ISLAND

*I*n the bleak darkness of the early morning the blaring PA system awakened Buster from a fitful night of interrupted sleep. The dull thudding in his temples and sour taste in his mouth were a glum reminder of his alcohol-enhanced carousing the night before. As the harsh glare of bare overhead bulbs showered the barracks, disgusted groans and shouted curses poured through the long barracks, beating harshly against Buster's aching head. His feet flat on the cool concrete floor, he sat, hands covering his eyes, blocking out the light. Wearing only navy issue skivvies, his muscled body was covered with a patina of sweat from the tropical heat. He wiped one hand across his bald head and his palm came away slick with it. With his damp thumbs he tried to massage away the pain in his temples. Scotch whiskey headaches were the worst, he thought.

"Come on you sleeping beauties, we've got work to do," yelled Richard Bell, the platoon leader, who was standing at the light switch.

"Chows on in fifteen minutes. And you better eat hearty. There's nothing but K-rations till after we've invaded Cat Island."

"Why don't you shut the hell up?" Buster said.

"Can't do that, Buster. Company D's already on Cat Island setting up a mock defense. Going to give us a taste of what it might look like when we'll really have to face enemy fire one of these days."

"What if those boys from Company D get the notion we're really Japs?" Buster bitched, not lifting his hands from his face, hating Bell's nasal whine.

"Then we'll give them one hell of a fight," said Johnny Polk, a large, dark-skinned man two bunks away. He was already dressed and ready for the day.

"Shut up Polk. My head hurts enough already without my having to hear you mouth off," Buster said.

Bell started down the narrow path between the bunks, swatting the iron frames with a baton. "Get your butt moving, Jenkins, so's you won't miss anything." He gave an extra hard whack to Buster's bunk and, as he continued on, catcalls and whistles followed him.

Pain rattled in Buster's head, and he had to restrain himself from wresting the baton from the man's hand and flattening his skull. If he ever caught him on the street after the war, Buster vowed he'd break both Bell's legs.

But Bell wasn't through yet. "Okay girls, listen up. During the mock invasion, a detail of our own men will be firing blanks at us while a squadron of planes from a nearby Coast Guard base will make false flybys, pretending to strafe and bomb. Some of you will go ashore and neutralize the enemy while the rest will haul ass and get our equipment ashore."

The whole idea was a pain in the ass as far as Buster was concerned. He briefly thought of going AWOL, taking off into town, hitting the bars and chasing the local women, then falling into one of their beds and passing out. Another sharp pain rocketed through his temple, forcing that thought out of his mind. Moving slowly not to disturb his brain, he dressed in his green fatigues and work boots, then shambled along behind the others to the mess hall, filled his plate, sat down at a table by himself, and devoured the syrup-drenched pancakes and greasy sausages on his plate.

Sitting before the empty plate, his lower lip pouched out, he stared at a spot somewhere in front of him, his mind blank to everything going on around him. Holding a smoldering cigarette between the two fingers he'd placed against his temple and supporting his jaw by the ball of his thumb, he let smoke curl about his face. He'd been in this godawful backwater less than two weeks, just got his legs back from that long boat ride from the U.S. to Trinidad. On March 23, 1943, the battalion had moved to Gulfport, Mississippi, and from there, on July 19, sailed toward Trinidad, seeing shipping blown up by Nazi subs and leaving Buster wondering the whole time if his ship was going to be next. And now he was going to have to get on another boat. He wished, not for the first time, that he'd walked away from that fight in Little Rock, Arkansas. The judge's decision, when Buster went before the bench, was that he could spend six months in jail or enlist. He'd enlisted and been assigned to the 80th Naval Construction Battalion when it was formed on January 26, 1943, in Camp Allen, at the Naval Operating Base, Norfolk, Virginia. Martha, his girlfriend, had told him he was lucky to be assigned to the SeaBees, which was made up of older men deemed fit to work but not fight. Though Buster attended service school for several weeks and learned military tactics; how to drill, how to salute, how a pistol, rifle, and machine-gun worked; what and what not to do with hand grenades; and that a bayonet was as potent a defensive weapon as it was an offensive one, he would likely never need any of that knowledge. He was thirty-five years and seven months old, well beyond the age they sent you into battle. Still, he wished he'd chosen the six months in jail. It couldn't have been that much worse than the service.

"You got that faraway look on your puss, Buster. You done deserted our little war party before we even sail?" Haug, an oil-driller from Ponca City, Oklahoma, slid in beside Buster and slapped him on the back.

"Damn. Don't do that."

"You thinking about last night? About Louisa? Right?"

"No. My head hurts too much to think about last night."

"Those were two pretty sweet items we found. We get back from this pleasure cruise to Cat Island, we got to try that again."

Buster looked down the row of tables at the scores of men finishing up their breakfasts and heading out the door to the loading docks. He again had a powerful urge to go AWOL, find that island girl he was with last night, and go native, leaving behind all his troubles back home and never looking back. "Why don't we just forget Cat Island and go find them right now."

"Come on. Get your lousy butt off that bench and let's go to work."

Big Johnny Polk was staring at him, eyes and face impassive, and he wondered what the SOB was thinking. "See that bastard, Polk over there? He's been getting under my skin since we left Norfolk."

"You better leave that one alone."

Buster smashed out his cigarette in the half-eaten pancake on a nearby plate. "Yea. Forget Polk. Let's go get this over with."

They loaded their ship and got underway, the water calm, a sea of glass that their tank-lighters and barges skimmed over in slow motion. Trucks, bulldozers, jeeps, field ranges and refrigerators, building materials crowded the decks. Men were perched on all the equipment or crowded together in small areas of the deck. German U-boats sometimes wandered through these waters, but most had been chased out, or, if present, Buster hoped they wouldn't waste their time on a light convoy like this one, without troopships, large battleships, or aircraft carriers. He sat in the shade of a tractor he would be driving ashore when they reached the island and smoked a Camel cigarette, blowing smoke that drifted up and, caught by the breeze, swirled crazily and disappeared.

As the dim form of Cat Island came into view, Richard Bell stepped onto a Caterpillar and yelled over the roar of the launch's motor, "Attention. Break out the K-rations."

Buster snuffed out his half-smoked cigarette and flipped it over the side. "Damn, but I'm going to be sick of SPAM before this miserable war is over." But he took out his rations and tore the lid from a dull army-green can, and began scooping the contents out with his fingers and sucking them into his mouth.

Hauk snorted. "You better enjoy that while you can. Won't be nothing else till we get all this crap on shore and set up for tomorrow."

Through scorching sunshine, the flat-bellied tank lighter approached Cat Island's sandy beach, waves battered the bow, rocking and rolling the craft. Three men grasped the side and lost their K-rations into the water. Tight-lipped, Buster braced himself against the rough treads of a tractor and, with a hundred other SeaBees of the 80th Construction Battalion, watched the palm-fringed island edge nearer. Over the bow Buster could see small puffs of smoke blossom as snipers in the palms began shooting blanks at the coxswains in the approaching craft. The pop of twenty-five-caliber rifles cut through the hum of the lighter's motor as the boat drove closer. Even knowing those weren't real bullets aimed at him, Buster swore, crouched down, and clenched his fists till his fingers cramped. In his shirt pocket he carried a letter he'd received from the States, one from Billy writing about peddling Grit papers on the streets of Hobart, earning money to buy war bonds, and worrying about Buster's safety. Billy sure as hell was more concerned about Buster right now than the navy brass sending him out here to help build an airbase in this godforsaken part of the world.

As the boat churned through the heavy surf, gallons of salt water poured in from the sides and splashed over Buster. "Goddamned. I'm going to drown before anybody has a chance to shoot me."

Johnny Polk, standing on the deck a few feet from him, spit into the water sloshing at their feet, and said to no one in particular, "This is a piece of cake. If them planes I hear comin' in was real Japs, you'd have something to gripe about."

"And you're talking from experience, now, aren't you?" Buster challenged.

"You got a mean streak, you know that?" said Polk.

Buster's hands tightened into fists but a low drone in the west made him glance at the sky where low-flying planes approached. He'd heard that in the Pacific theater on a clear day the strafing was worse than living in hell. He touched his shirt pocket, felt Billy's letter resting there, now most likely wet as a dishrag. Still, it might help him through the next few days without getting run over by a bulldozer or having a loose tool fall out of a tower and brain him. He'd like to tell Billy just that.

Bell, the platoon leader, not even old enough to be Buster's younger brother, stood on the back of a bulldozer, and brayed out loud as an overloaded mule, "Okay. Let's go. Mount those machines, boys."

Buster's numbed legs would hardly let him move onto the tractor. He knew this was all make-believe, but he felt a knot form in his stomach and his pulse quicken. He took a deep breath and held it, feeling his heart bucking inside his chest like a skittish stallion.

"Come on, you wet bastards, let's move." Bell shook his fist at them. "We gotta get those damn machines and supplies ashore." As if Buster were deaf, dumb, and blind, he repeated, "You heard me, Jenkins, get that tractor started."

Muttering curses, Buster mounted the tractor; then, praying that the salty water hadn't drowned out the ignition, brought the engine to life with one turn of the starter. Sitting high, with a full view of the beach, he caught sight of the first ones on shore flinging themselves down at the edge of the jungle, and then, crouching low and firing blanks, disappear into the maze of palms. It was a brief skirmish. All the "enemies" not tagged faded back into the groves. High in a palm tree, a sniper hung from his harness, his arms splayed and flapping as if he were ready to take flight as he waved at the incoming men.

The lighters slid to a halt in soft sand and the ramps dropped. As Buster drove the tractor ashore, he could hear the pop-pop-pop of automatic weapons as the soldiers set up a defensive arc somewhere close inland. A box of supplies, left too near the water, awash in the incoming lighters' wake, heaved further onto the sand. On the beaches of California, Buster had observed the surf playing with dead fish and driftwood. Had this been for real, that box could be some Seabee's dead body. Bile rose in the back of Buster's throat.

Shivering in the ninety-degree heat, he dismounted from the tractor and began to help unload mesh to lay down in the sand so the heavier equipment could drive inland. Commander White, USNR Civil Engineer from Tulsa, a pint-sized son-of-a-bitch with the energy of a jackhammer, moved up and down the beach, prodding them on like a slave master. Under his breath, Buster cursed White, the Japanese, the sun, and the lighters that, in an endless stream, delivered men and supplies to the beach. The mesh in place, he drove his tractor off the lighter into the midst of trucks, heavy guns, ammunition, and other supplies that littered the beach. The mesh he'd helped unload, designed to "snowshoe" vehicles over soft sand or mud, failed and his tractor bogged down. Supplies couldn't be ferried inland with the tractors or Cats so Buster and the others loaded barrels and packages onto their backs and plowed barefoot through the sand to the depots. Soaked to the skin with his own sweat, he shucked his pants and shirt and soon, every man around him threw off his and worked in skivvies. The other men, also slick with sweat and struggling through the mushy sand, reminded Buster of the slimy bullfrogs living back home in his pa's rocky draw. As the sun burned his skin darker, Buster wiped sweat from his eyes, cursed his slick hands, and somehow kept on. When more mesh was laid down, he started up his tractor again and, weaving his way through the supplies on shore, he reached the jungle's edge and parked just inside. He unslung his rifle from where he'd stashed it on the tractor, stood up, and pointed, pretending to shoot at a tree.

"Careful there. You goin' to shoot yourself in the foot."

"Damn, Polk. Don't sneak up on me that way again or I'll shoot you a new asshole."

"I'll remember that," the big man said. "And shoot first."

"To hell with you, Polk."

The big man laughed and walked back toward the lighter.

Sitting back down on the hard metal seat of the tractor, a memory came to Buster of Twilla and the first time he'd taken her on a buggy-ride. The thought pained him. He wanted to forget all they'd gone through together, leave it behind him, and turn all his thoughts to Martha. But sometimes he missed Twilla, Sarah May, and Billy. That was the damn problem. When he'd received Billy's letter two days before, he'd changed his mind about leaving them. Decided to let Martha fend for herself. But then he'd opened Martha's letter and reading it had nearly torn his heart out. Angry, he went back to work.

They unloaded six ships before sundown. Countless Seabees waded onto the island and when night had wrapped the shore in darkness so black he couldn't see his hand in front of his face, Buster was allowed to stop. Exhausted and grit-covered, he looked but couldn't find a place in the dark to set up shelter, so he rolled up in his tent on the sand and tried to sleep. Night birds called out and insects set up a hum, a racket that reminded him of summer nights in Oklahoma when the cicadas sang. His mama had once told him she'd thought the sound of cicadas was a motor that turned the world. Out in the dark of this world, infested with men who would like nothing better than to kill him, he hoped she was right. Maybe those thousands of insects would keep his world going.

Before he could drift off into sleep, he heard loud yells that stopped as suddenly as they started. They were shrill, like those of a wounded hog, a wild razorback he'd once heard just before his pa put a bullet through its brains. But he was too exhausted to do more than roll over and ask, "What the hell was that, Hauk?"

"Damned SeaBees from D Company, playing like Japs, trying to infiltrate. Sounds like our boys out in the grove are after them. Probably scared the shit out of them, somebody grabbing them in the dark."

"Son of a bitch."

Next day, before the sun bore down, Buster pulled himself from sleep and began the endless unloading, making short trips ferrying supplies with his tractor to the jungle's edge on a jury-rigged sled. From there, other men hand-carried them further into the grove. He helped load ammunition for the 155s and then headed the tractor for the tree line. Halfway there, the mesh gave way under the front wheels and the tractor bucked, the front end rearing up and throwing Buster to the ground. The engine stalled and Buster lay stunned, his ears ringing louder than any cicadas that had ever filled a night with sound. Someone grabbed his shoulder and shook him, called his name, too, though it sounded as if the words came from a long distance. He sat up, spat, and looked around.

Hauk stood over him, shouting, "Shit, man. I saw that son-of-bitching thing throw you off. Thought sure as hell you was dead."

Still dazed, Buster shook his head, trying to clear the swirling edges of his mind. "I hit a damned weak spot in the mesh."

"That bastard had jumped much higher it'd come back over on you. Killed you deader'n a doornail."

"Christ." Buster stood and balanced himself against a tree. "I'm so tired I could sleep right here."

"Don't count on it." Hauk pointed out to sea, which was covered with landing craft carrying more men and supplies. "There comes more work."

"Okay, you two goof-offs," Bell called. "Leave that tractor where it is and get back down to shore and help get those incoming lighters unloaded."

"You SOB. Say one more word to me and I'll coldcock you, I swear," Buster said.

"Come on, Buster. Let it lie." Hauk started walking toward a lighter that had come in to shore. "Let's just get these unloaded so we can go to bed."

Buster followed Hauk to the ocean's edge and washed his face. The dizziness and ringing in his ears had almost stopped by the time he reached for a barrel handed from off the lighter. He wrestled it onto the beach and then began rolling it toward the palm-trees. A man, sitting on the sand, stared, frozen in place as though playing one of those childhood games Buster had joined in where he had to stand like a statue until rescued by a friend. A medic came by and led the man off toward the dispensary tent, which had been pitched only moments before. Buster felt a moment's envy; the war was probably over for this guy. He wondered what shape he'd have found himself in if this had been a real invasion, with men dying and him being shot at, wounded—killed.

A rich smell drifted into his nose, took him from his reveries and propelled him toward camp, which was springing up out of the sand, tents growing like mushrooms to be used for the armory, tool crib, officers' quarters, field headquarters, and mess. Cooks were standing over hot field-ranges frying SPAM. Steam roiled from great vats of boiled potatoes. Lines of men had already formed when Buster joined Hauk near the front of the line, pretending not to hear the catcalls and grumbling of the men behind him.

Johnny Polk, who had worked alongside Buster most of the day, though neither had said more to the other than was necessary, tapped Buster on the shoulder. "How's come some of us act special when he ain't done no more work than the rest?"

"Go blow it out your ass, Johnny. Hauk was saving me a place."

"Likes of you makes me wonder why I'm helping fight this war."

"Hell, the government shouldn't let the likes of you even fight." Buster shot back.

Hauk handed Buster a tray, shoving it hard into his midsection. "You gonna exercise your gums arguing here or are we going to eat?"

Buster turned and walked down the line as mashed potatoes, meat and green beans were ladled onto his tray.

"You a hard case, Jenkins," Johnny Polk called after him.

Buster shrugged and did not answer.

As night fell, Buster, leaning against a tree beside his tent, lit up a cigarette and took a deep drag. "Hauk, when you're past thirty, you have one helluva time working all day and then getting up in the morning."

"Hell, there isn't a man on this island that's younger than thirty. This damn war machine they talk about would get stuck up to its axles if it weren't for all of us SeaBees who're too damn old to fight."

Buster nodded and brushed at sand on his forearm. "It's damn hard keeping clean on this sandpile."

Hauk lit up two cigarettes and passed one to Buster. "Them navy boys aboard ship take a shower, wash down with antiseptic, and put on clean clothes before they go to work."

"Yea, join the Air Force and you can have a bath before taking off in one of those fancy planes."

"We get killed, it's usually up to our elbows in sand. Or mud."

"If I die, I don't want to be buried in this stinking sandpile." Buster took a deep drag and let the smoke slowly dribble out his nose, as if he could parcel it out till the end of the war, keeping his sanity and not dying.

"When you die, you die. Clean or dirty." Hauk pitched his half-smoked cigarette into the sand and turned to sleep. "And you don't quit baiting people like Polk, you might just die sooner'n you expect."

"Jesus H. Christ, Hauk, you're a sour son-of-a-bitch."

Next day, practically before he'd closed his eyes, Buster was shouted awake by Bell and with the rest of the half-awake men, led off to the mess hall. After wolfing their pancakes, washed down with scalding black coffee, they were made to report to the company commander who assigned the company the job of building a road across the island to a second camp already in place. A coconut grove lay just back of the beach, and, as Buster's detachment began cutting down trees, they sank into sand so soft that only the biggest Caterpillars could get through. Mosquitoes sniped at them as they advanced, felling coconut palms, cutting them into twelve-foot lengths, and corrugating the road. The traction-treaded Cats could then drive over the logs, but the spinning wheels of the ten-wheeled trucks sent the logs flying and they buried themselves to the axles. They had to be dragged along by the cats.

By the midafternoon, the log road was open to the other end of the island where the second camp lay bathed in tropical heat. Diesel oil and gasoline drums lay about everywhere. To help move the inflammable stuff back into the storage areas under construction, Buster fell in line with other men in a bucket brigade and, for hours, passed heavy packages and drums back into the camouflage area, the piles sinking deeper into the sand with each passage. Mosquitoes dive-bombed him and gnats hovered around his face, waiting turns to suicide into his pale blue eyes, the whites of which were burning red from the blowing sand and baking sun.

As the sun receded on the second day, Buster forced down his supper and then fell into his bedroll, pulled his mosquito netting about him, and passed into sleep, not responding to Hauk's mumbled goodnight.

By the end of the third day all the gun emplacements were finished, the radio mast, the one-thousand-barrel oil storage tank, the ammunition magazine, and the administration tent were near completion. The landing strip had been smoothed and made ready for the pierced-planking surface to be laid down. Only the ten-thousand-barrel storage tank was behind schedule by day's end and Buster was put to work with every other available Seabee to get it finished so they could return to Gulfport the next day. Buster had spent an eighteen-hour shift, taking only short rests for food before being put to work again. He cursed under his breath at gung-ho Richard Bell, five years younger, who pushed Buster to the limit. He was more than ever ready to catch him out behind a tent somewhere and wipe up the sand with his worthless carcass. At moments in the late afternoon he would have done just that if he hadn't been so bone-tired. Stumbling back toward camp in the early evening, one of the men jerked off his clothes and jumped into the water and began splashing at the rest. Buster stood on shore a moment watching as dozens of tired men shed clothes and ran headlong into the waves. With a yell, he dove into the water, clothes and all, and came up behind Hauk, grabbed him and pushed him under.

Hauk came up gasping and sputtering. "You crazy son of a bitch. You trying to drown me?"

"If I did, I wouldn't have to hear you snore all night, would I?" Buster grabbed for Hauk again but missed, stumbling and falling forward in the water.

Hauk gripped Buster by the scruff of the neck. "You're the one that snores," he said, and forced Buster under, holding him a few seconds before letting go.

Buster came up coughing and spitting and then swung at Hauk, catching him on the shoulder and sending him staggering back. "You bastard. You did damn near drown me."

Hauk drew back to throw a punch of his own but pulled up short when his name was called.

Richard Bell, the platoon leader called out again, "Hauk. Jenkins. You two, cut it out. And the rest of you. Out of there, now. We got to get back before it gets too dark."

Buster splashed toward shore, kicking water as he went, sending a geyser spraying over Bell. "Whoops. Sorry." He stood grinning, daring Bell to react.

Instead, Bell stared, his eyes mean. "You're pressing your luck with me, you worthless shit."

Buster took a step closer to Bell and stood nose to nose. "I think maybe you're coming close to running out of luck yourself."

Hauk grabbed Buster from behind and carried him in a bear hug back to where Hauk's clothes lay in the sand. "I don't want you to spend the rest of this bloody war in the stockade. Who'd I go drinking with?" He spilled Buster onto the sand. "You punch me again, though, by God, and I'll bury your sorry ass six feet in the sand."

Buster took three deep breaths and stood, sand covering his work blues and hands. He brushed at his clothes, then walked back to the water and rinsed himself off before falling in behind the last man in his platoon and trudging off to the mess hall.

In the dark, as he lay still, trying to fall asleep under mosquito netting that seemed to hold in the heat of the night, he heard a rustling outside his tent and then his name whispered. Looking outside, he saw by the moonlight several men milling around.

Richard Bell stood close to the tent. "Jenkins? Come on out here. I want to talk to you."

Buster turned, shook Hauk awake and pointed outside. "I think there's a posse out there. You coming with me?"

"Sure. Wouldn't want to miss a hanging."

Buster pulled on his pants and walked out, his bare back and shoulder shining with sweat. "What's up, Bell?"

"You've been aching for a fight ever since you joined this platoon, Jenkins. I figure you're not going to be happy till you get one."

Buster felt a thrill of anticipation and fear as he looked at the other men of his platoon standing around, looking expectant. He wondered if he had a friend among them other than Hauk. He hadn't hidden his dislike for them. "Am I going to have to whip the whole bunch of you?"

Bell gave a short laugh. "No. But I suspect you could have your pick of any one of them, you take a notion. They're all sick of you." Bell turned and led the way through the dark to an open space on the beach where he took a pair of boxing gloves from Polk. "Polk here has graciously volunteered to do the honors."

"You don't fight your own fights?"

Johnny Polk, his muscled, bare chest gleaming from sweat in the moonlight, stepped closer. "I made it my fight too. None of us here cotton to the way you treat us."

Buster looked at Johnny Polk and then took the gloves, never taking his eyes off him or Bell. He walked away from the group several feet, and held his gloved hands out to Hauk who tied them tightly to his wrists. "This SOB is going to make mincemeat out of me, Hauk," he whispered. "And he isn't even the one I'm wanting the most to see whipped."

Hauk shook his head. "You haven't exactly hid your feelings about the likes of Polk. He don't miss seeing that. Probably talked Bell into it."

"Bell's a bloody Nazi, you ask me. It's his ass I want to kick."

"Just go on over there and take it like a man. Probably won't last too long, so you ain't going to suffer too much."

"That all the encouragement I'm going to get?" Buster walked over to where Bell and Johnny Polk stood ringed by most of the men. There was an excited quiver in his stomach. He remembered the time him and Richard had whipped the three Horton brothers, big farm boys with eyes meaner than Johnny Polk's or Bell's. Of course, Richard had had to use a scoop shovel to brain one of them to make it a fair fight.

Bell, his mouth twisted into a sour grin, his white teeth glowing in the moonlight, stepped between Johnny Polk and Buster.

"There ain't going to be any kicking or biting. First man down can end the fight by not getting up. Or not being able to get up. Any questions?"

Buster spat close to Bell's shoe. "I got one. Why aren't you fighting your own fight?"

"Polk volunteered. Figured he'd give you a better fight than me."

"You say the first man down who won't or can't get up loses?"

"That's what I said. You ready?"

Buster brought his punch up from the waist and caught Bell square on the chin, then followed with a left jab to the eye. The man dropped like a shot hog and lay still. Johnny Polk stood, hands poised to fight, still as a board, as if it had been him who was stunned and lying on the ground.

Hauk gave a loud guffaw and stepped between Buster and Johnny Polk. "You boys heard the rules. First man down and don't get up, loses. I declare Buster Jenkins the winner here. Now, let's all get some sleep."

Johnny Polk slid the gloves off and pointed down at Bell. "What we gonna do with this one? Can't leave him out here all night."

Buster poked Bell with his shoe and got no response. "You want to grab his legs while I get his arms? We'll carry him to his bunk. If I'm lucky, he'll sleep all night before he comes after my ass."

Johnny Polk reached down and bodily hefted Bell across his broad shoulders. "Don't need no help."

Stung, Buster balled his fist but thought better of pushing his luck by saying something back. He considered Johnny Polk not much better than an animal, but he was a damned dangerous animal.

As the platoon, almost every man wearing a knowing grin, formed up the next morning, Buster stood at attention with the rest, darting glances out of the corner of his eyes at Bell who sported a black eye and bruised jaw. He'd half expected the MPs to come calling that morning as he crawled, bleary-eyed, from a restless night of sleep, from his tent.

Bell stepped to the front of the men and cleared his throat. "Okay, men, we're loading up our gear to get out of here by sundown. Our detail is to break camp and start loading the galley equipment, gear, and rolling stock aboard the barges. Jenkins, Hauk, you're to report to the detail working on the storage tank. Any questions?" When there were none, he dismissed the platoon and Bell and the other men moved off, leaving Buster and Hauk standing together.

"I guess he plans to work us to death instead of throwing us to the Military Police," Buster said.

"Probably didn't want the brass to know he put Polk up to beating your brains out. And he sure doesn't want it to be known any more'n it already is that you made a jackass out of him in front of his men."

"Let's get out of here before he changes his mind."

As darkness fell on the day the platoon arrived back in Gulfport, the barracks were empty except for Buster who stood guard duty and Hauk who was the last to leave for weekend liberty.

"Sorry, pal, but I guess losing liberty on our first night back is better than sitting in the stockade for a month."

"Tell Louisa why I won't be showing up."

"Hell, no. I'm going to tell her you said I should look out for her because you'll be doing guard duty for the duration."

"You do that and I'll break this rifle over your head."

Hauk laughed. "See you, buddy."

Left alone at his post, Buster stood at parade rest, his legs beginning to ache. He tried to hold on to images of Louisa, but instead, his mind wandered to what he was going home to when the war was over. He had sat with his pa and cried like a baby for weeks before being called up. "What am I to do?" he'd asked, over and over again. His pa didn't know and his ma wouldn't say. The question still nagged, should he stay with Twilla, Sarah May and Billy? Or with Martha? How could he make that decision? There was no way he could see clear to make such a choice.

He thought to himself, it might be ten years before the war was over and he saw Oklahoma or Arkansas again. Maybe by then either Martha or Twilla would forget him and go with somebody. Probably not.

Or maybe before the war was over the Japs, Johnny Polk or one of his kind—or Richard Bell—would see to it he never made it home. That thought didn't cheer him at all.

Nine months later, the 80th returned to the States, arriving at Camp Endicott, Davisville, Rhode Island, on May 13th. In June, they departed for Camp Rousseau at Port Hueneme, California, arriving sometime in early June and remaining there eleven months. On May 18, 1945, the 80th sailed for Subic Bay in the Philippines, arriving on June 16 and remaining until the end of the war. They returned to the United States sometime between August 15, when Emperor Hirohito agreed to surrender, and September 29, 1945.

Buster survived Polk, the Japs, and court martial and returned with his battalion.

He was honorably discharged from service in Sampson, New York, on September 29, 1945. At the time of discharge, he was listed as a Carpenter's Mate 1c (CB) V6 USNR and was thirty-eight years and four months old. There's no history as to how or when he made his decision, but he decided to live with Martha, and during the next several years fathered more children who grew to adulthood, but only seeing Billy and Sarah May a few times. As adults, all four of his children learned to love and respect one another and were thankful that whatever faults Buster may have had, and they were many, he did pick good women to father children with.

FAMILY ENTERTAINMENT

It was Wednesday, April 30, 1976, when, bored and a bit lonely, Perry left his room at the Lord Baltimore Hotel, walked out into the cool night air, and hailed a yellow cab. He crawled into the back seat and was greeted by a gruff, to-the-point question, "Where to?" The words issued from a mouth buried in massive jowls, and if there was a smile or a scowl it was lost in the folds of his heavy brow and bulging chins. The driver was so huge that the bottom of the steering wheel was buried in his stomach, and Perry wondered how the man could turn it to steer. His pale, hairy arms, untouched by the sun, were like two thick, unbaked, sesame seed loaves hanging from a large, doughy body.

In answer to his question, Perry said, "When I came from the airport, I noticed some movie theaters a few blocks from here. I'd like to ride over and find out if there's a film I'd like to see."

The cabbie pulled down the flag and set the cab in motion, then twisted partly around. His head, covered with a mass of black curly hair and set on a massive neck, was so armored in his own flesh that his whole body had to turn when he made the effort to catch Perry's eye.

"You know, I'm not sure you want to go to a movie in that part of town. It's a bit dangerous. The only movie theaters I'd go to are out in the burbs." The big head shook back and forth in denial of Perry's wish.

By then, in only a short two blocks, they had passed into an area where the street was littered and the buildings dingy. Even the darkness could not hide the squalor of the neighborhood. A knot of young men or teenagers stood on a dark corner scowling as they passed. Perry leaned forward and put his arm on the back of the front seat so the cabbie could better hear him and said, "I see what you mean. Looks a bit creepy around here."

The cabbie laughed, knowingly. "Ain't it the truth." He wheeled the cab left and started down a street empty of people.

"You're a stranger to Baltimore," he stated.

"My first trip." To himself the thought occurred, I am a stranger and I don't really want to be one, tonight. But here I am alone and with nothing to do.

"You sounded like weren't from around here."

"Yea, I was born and raised in Kansas . . . just visiting for a few days."

"You here for a meeting?"

"Yeah." Perry said nothing about his Christian Brotherhood meeting, not wanting to encourage a conversation. Speaking religion or politics to strangers had gotten him into arguments in the past. He didn't want that tonight. Instead, he asked, "Are there any safe theaters or shows in Baltimore you could drive me to?"

FAMILY ENTERTAINMENT

The driver pulled the cab to a stop at the curb of a deserted street corner and pushed the shift into park. "No. People don't come downtown anymore for that sort of thing. You have to go a long way out."

He scratched thoughtfully at his hairy arm for a moment. The quietness of the deserted street seemed to drift in through the open front window of the cab, an eerie stillness. It was as if he were in a cemetery, the buildings sitting around like tombstones. There was a rush of sound as a lone car passed and, far off, on the river, a ship's horn blared faintly. A man walked past, hurrying, his footsteps magnified by the otherwise unreal silence. The car, with its motor idling but inaudible, sent ghostly tendrils of exhaust fumes dancing across the untended street. Perry felt spooked.

Encased as he was in body fat, like armor, the cabbie couldn't hold Perry's gaze for long but had to keep swiveling his head, throwing back quick glances like baseballs from a batting machine.

"There is a place on Pulaski Road. Called Sherry's Show Bar. I take the little lady there sometimes. Not a bad place to spend an evening."

Was "the little lady" his wife? Girlfriend? Whichever, the thought of any little lady with this mountain of a man would be a sight and made Perry want to laugh, but he kept a straight face. "What's it like?"

"They got a little band that plays. Not too high class. But good music and some dancing."

Perry was tempted to go, but then wondered how much chance there was that the cabbie might be setting him up for a long ride and a large fare. He was lonely, though, and wanted something to do other than sit in a hotel room reading all evening. Or watching television. And he wanted to get the cab moving, away from the tomb-like silence of the solitary street. Making up his mind, he said, "Sounds okay to me."

"Then let's have a go at Sherry's." Once said, the cabbie ground the shift into gear and they drove on, heading south to Baltimore Street, past the hotels Baltimore Hilton and the Lord Baltimore where Perry was staying. On seeing the lighted entrance after the gloom of the street they'd been on, he had the impulse to direct the hefty driver to stop at the hotel and let him out, but he stifled it. What actual danger was he in? I have a concerned guide who saved me from a ghetto movie, he thought to himself. He'll look after me.

They sped through a cityscape in transition, passing barricades where new construction was underway, and buildings of modern design pushing up amid old structures like brightly colored and symmetrical mushrooms sprouting from the dead and decaying organic residues of the past.

"This here is the heart of Baltimore," the cabbie called over his shoulder. "A bunch of tobacco farmers asked the state legislature for sixty acres of land to start a town. That was back in 1729. They've been building and tearing down and rebuilding again ever since."

"Looks like it's in a growing stage now," Perry said. "Probably lots of new restaurants."

"That's right. But we got some good, old restaurants around here, too. Been here for ages. You got to go to Obryki's over in the Fells Point. No other restaurant in Baltimore serves crabs like Obryki's. You being from Kansas, I bet you never had fresh steamed crabs."

"I'm afraid not," Perry confessed.

"Well, you're in for a treat. Good beer and steamed crabs. Nothing can beat that. But don't eat the devil's meat."

Was there no place one could go where they would be safe from the concepts of good and evil, God and the devil? God's crabmeat and devil's crabmeat? "What is devil's meat?" Perry asked.

"I don't know how exactly to describe it but, after you've cracked open the shell and pulled the cover off the meat, there are some little dark pieces that peel off like orange slices. You don't eat that."

"How come?" Perry wasn't satisfied with a simple admonition. "Is it poison?"

"I don't know," the cabbie confessed. "I just know my mother always told me, 'Don't eat the devil's meat.' That's all I know." He drove on in silence, no doubt thinking of his mother.

That figures, Perry thought; my concepts of good and evil went back to my mother telling me to beware of the devil that lived under the kitchen sink and would come out to get naughty boys. Now I suspect she told me that to keep me away from the poisonous household products children are sometimes prone to sample. Needless to say, I never opened the door beneath the kitchen sink. But he said none of this to the cabbie.

They passed Light and Calvert Streets and bright lights came into view ahead as they passed a sign announcing Gay Street.

"That's The Block up ahead on Baltimore Street," the cabbie said, "You don't want to go to The Block, ever."

"Why not?"

"The Block's a pretty bad area. There's just a lot of sleazy joints there. It isn't any different than what you'd have found in Nam, or Singapore, or Seoul; any large seaport. You'll find them places all over the world. Now you being a stranger from out West, you probably never been in any seaport towns or saw a place like The Block, so I wouldn't recommend you go there by yourself. They'll really hustle you. Sell you liquor for ten-twenty dollars a bottle and all you get is a buck twenty-five bottle of Cold Duck. And take those girls, now. They'll come up and put their hands on your lap and say, 'I love you,' and shit like that."

Having indeed never seen a place like The Hook, Perry experienced a prurient curiosity about such goings on. At his grand old age of forty-two, he'd never been to a strip joint. A wave of guilt washed away the curiosity.

"This is the middle of The Block," the cabbie said and reduced his speed. "Used to be a little hook of land jutting out into the river here. Folks say that's where the word, 'hooker,' came from 'cause there was so many whorehouses here. The hook's gone but you can sure bet the hookers haven't."

They cruised past bar after bar decorated by animated neon signs that pictured women dancers with flashing red legs and blinking flesh-colored breasts and shimmying behinds, a light show to attract the attention of any male wandering by. On the streets he could see well-dressed young business types in suits and ties, black dudes with brass-studded pants and coats, shabbily dressed bums, hoodlums with slicked back hair and hard eyed men in washed cotton denims but no flesh-and-blood women.

Perry wondered if there really were any live woman on The Block or were all the females just glimmering, neon-light dancers festooning the buildings' marquee? He had a fantasy that if he held out his hand to one of the seductive, dancing light-women, she might walk away with him to her room where she would dazzle his senses with her garish light. How silly he thought, then said, "I don't see any women on the streets."

"They're all working inside the bars. No decent woman would come down here. The cabbie slowed even more and pointed a finger, large as a bratwurst, toward an open door, "There's some sitting at the tables in there. See them? They're the ones who'll try to con you into buying them cheap watered-down booze. I wouldn't advise you to go into those kinds of bars."

Perry could see actual flesh-and-blood women inside the bars as they drifted by one open doorway after another, each scene coming into view and then giving way to the next, offering the impression of movement like that he had seen in his youth while thumbing the pages of Little Big Books. The flickering images of the gyrating female bodies, each glance revealing an altered pose and a different degree of undress—a seamless moving act. On stages built high above gaping men, women were offered up to the hungry gaze of scores of voyeurs, some sitting with other scantily clothed partners who, the cabbie had said, laid their hands close to inflamed passions and told endearing lies. Those were places he had never attended nor did he have any desire to prowl down these littered streets, whose decrepit buildings seemed to stand only by the grace of the unnumbered coats of paint hardened on their ancient wood and brick. He had no wish to taste this experience. He thought of eating crabs but not their devil's meat. This area had to be Baltimore's devil's meat. "You're right, I wouldn't want to visit The Hook."

"Yea, I've been around a few seaport towns and there's no rougher section than a riverfront strip like The Block."

Now past The Block, they sped up on their way to a friendly neighborhood bar where the cabbie brought his little lady, and the worst he would be subjected to was some bad music. "You mentioned Nam, Singapore . . . you were in the navy?"

"Naw, the marines. I was in the service for four years. That's how I could afford to get my cab. I saved my money." He paused as though to remember the experience. "I'd probably still be in the army if they hadn't sold us out."

Perry didn't respond to that statement. He'd felt being at war was a dreadful waste, but didn't want to antagonize the man by saying so. "So, when you got out, you bought a cab, huh?"

"Yea, I saved up about twenty-five thousand dollars, not all of it legit, you understand. I was into a little black-market stuff. But I came out with that money and came back here, bought myself a medallion and a cab. They gave it to me cheaper, you understand, 'cause I was a vet and all. The things cost twenty-five to thirty grand then, but I got mine for fifteen. But now they nickel and dime me to death—dues to the Association, insurance . . . and gas. You wouldn't believe the gas I buy . . . at least twenty to thirty gallons a day and sometimes as much as forty to fifty." He stopped talking as he wheeled the cab around an area where construction crews had made deep holes in the pavement, abandoning his full attention on the inequity of the gas prices and giving it to the dangers of potholes.

Perry sat back in the seat for a moment realizing how tense he was, riding to God knows where and having no knowledge of this man who had just admitted to being into the illegal black market overseas. Was he, indeed, being taken for a ride? Hoodwinked? Was there really a Sherry's Show Bar? He asked, "Do we have much further to go?"

"Naw, it's not too far now. We'll be there in another few minutes. I'm through for the day. I wouldn't mind stoppin' off for a beer right now myself."

There was a thinly disguised invitation in that last comment and by now Perry was a bit intimidated so he asked, "Why don't you let me buy you a drink then?"

"Hell, why not? Thanks." The cabbie reached out a meaty hand and shoved the meter flag down with a flourish. "Hell, since you're a stranger and I'm on my way home, anyway, this ride's on me."

Perry started to object to the free ride and then thought better of it. He had been proffered a free ride after he offered a free drink. Why should he be any less gracious in accepting generosity? "Thanks, I appreciate that," Perry offered.

"Hey, that's okay. My pleasure." The cabbie strained around and offered his hand, dwarfing Perry's. "I'm Jack."

"I'm Perry."

"Nice to know you, Perry," Jack said as he wheeled into a Standard Oil station parking area and came to a stop. "That's Sherry's over there," he said.

A lone, dingy building sat close to the curb, its front door close to the eastbound traffic on Pulaski Road. The building was long and narrow and had probably once shared the block with other small buildings that had been torn down to make way for the service station where they had just parked. The weak light from a dim bulb over the entrance revealed that the door had most likely been painted sometime shortly after the turn of the century.

"Let me give the guy at the station a couple of bucks to park here." He heaved himself out the taxi door with a great huff of breath and waddled over to the service station door, leaving the cab's motor running.

Perry stepped from the cab wondering what he'd got himself into. Out of loneliness and boredom, he had let this hulk of a man talk him into coming to some dive out in the middle of nowhere.

Jack brought his massive body back to the car, reached inside, and switched off the ignition. "Let's go. They're goin' to be starting the first show in just a little while."

Well, you've come this far, you might as well go on in, Perry thought. Surely it can't be any worse than sitting back in my hotel. And Jack is a character of sorts, even if a less than honest one. He saved me from the ghetto movies, didn't he? He didn't charge me for the ride, did he? I did promise him a drink, didn't I? Perry fell into step with Jack.

On entering the painted door Jack waved his jackhammer hand in a sweeping gesture, taking in the whole of the long, narrow room with a high ceiling. "This is it," he said, mightily pleased with his choice of an entertainment establishment. Passing up the twelve or more small tables crammed against the back wall, he led the way to the bar and perched heavily, and, Perry thought, precariously, on one of the high stools. His enormous thighs hung over, taking up room enough for three.

Perry sat down beside Jack at the bar, a half circle of old oak fronting a twelve-foot-wide and eight-foot-deep stage sitting even with the top of the bar. In one corner there was a small organ and drum trap. Fly-specked pictures of long-dead jazz artists stretched along the length of the back wall. The dusty and unvarnished stage floor was occupied by a large calico cat which raised its head when Jack sat down. For a moment it stared at them in that disdainful and distant way that any well-bred cat will do. It half closed and opened its eyes wide, never taking its gaze from Jack and Perry who thought of the musical, *Cats*, and the character that played the old and faded star. The calico was like that, a famous old artist in a run-down bar, though it did add some dignity to the decay. Perry fantasied that it was one of the performers and wondered how good a voice it had. After regarding them and apparently satisfied that they were well beneath its further notice, it lowered its feline head and went back to its interrupted nap.

The bar room could have seated forty people but there were only a few couples seated about; one a slight, blond man and a young woman with him who sat turned away with her head bowed. Though it was chilly in the room the man wore only jeans and a "Dead" T-shirt, and had goosebumps running up and down his arms. He was talking earnestly with the woman who had on a short dress and no stockings and goosebumps on her legs that matched those on the man's arm. Their half-whispered words did not carry. She was not obviously responding to his words but her shoulders trembled once as if she were racked with sobs, and the blond man patted her shoulder. After a moment he stood and came behind the counter saying, "What will it be, Jack?"

Perry was reassured. At least Jack was known here.

"Give us a couple of beers, Joe." Jack held up two doughy bread stick fingers as he spoke, and it wasn't clear whether he was giving the victory sign or accenting his request.

The man nodded and walked to a chest, looked back without opening its lid and inquired, "You want a Budweiser, Michelob, or a Schlitz?" It was obvious from his short list that variety in drink was not of great importance in this establishment.

Jack smiled serenely at Perry, waiting for him to choose. "Make mine a Bud," Perry responded, sounding like an actor in a beer commercial. Jack echoed the request.

Joe bent over, lifted the ice chest's lid, and with the clink and swish of bottles being pulled from out of crushed ice, brought forth two Buds. He set them on the closed lid and dried them with a white rag, his caress of the bottles as tender as it had been when he comforted the young woman still hunched on her stool, her back to them. Cold fumes roiled out of the bottles as they were opened and the fresh, sour smell of beer spilled out. From a rack where scores of clear glasses stood like soldiers at parade rest, the barman took two glasses, and stood a moment polishing water spots from their surfaces. As he poured, he cast brief glances at the back of the forlorn lady. Behind him, an army of whiskey bottles stood at attention, their necks coming only to the height of the stage so as not to interfere with a view of the stage.

Perry hastily took out money, and paid for the beers. After all, he had invited Jack to have a beer—and the big man hadn't charged for the cab ride.

"Thanks," Jack said and then launched unprovoked into a story about Nam.

"People are the same the world over. You make friends with them and they treat you decent. I was in a lot of those peoples' homes overseas. Ate their food, too, though I didn't like it. One of the first things I would do when I went into a village would be to throw candy bars to the kids. The grownups appreciated that. You do a person a favor and they do you one. That's the way it works in this damn world." He sat contemplating that fact of life for a few seconds.

When Perry didn't respond to his philosophizing, Jack turned to the blond man, who was now huddled with the distraught woman, and asked, "What time is the show going to start tonight, Joe?"

Joe turned and smiled. "It'll be thirty minutes or so, Jack. Some of the people got here late." He then went back to comforting his unhappy companion.

Jack turned back to Perry. "I think Della's plowed. She's the regular bartender here but she ain't doing much tending tonight. I never saw Joe tending before."

Perry thought more customers were arriving when the door opened and a woman of indeterminate age entered the bar. Her makeup was so thick it could have been dipped off with a spoon. Hair done up in a high bouffant and clothes, gaudy but expensive, were totally out of keeping with the flip-flops slapping against bare feet. She was followed by a younger man of fifty or so, whose face was covered with a scraggly fuzz. He had an expensive coat hung on one thin arm and his neatly pressed trousers bagged about sparse buttocks. His pants cuffs barely reached the thin bare ankles that were attached to feet sporting thongs that tapped out an accompanying rhythm to that of his female companion's footwear.

The calico raised its head to watch, but did not move until the man called, "Here puss, come to daddy, Jellico." The stage-cat rose leisurely and strolled nonchalantly to him, less impressed with the reunion than was the man. He picked the animal up and buried his face in its luxuriant fur as he and the woman, thongs slapping, disappeared into the back.

"Those are the owners, Sherry and Alfred," Jack volunteered when the door closed behind them.

As soon as the trio had vanished, Joe jumped to his feet and looked anxiously at the door that had closed behind them. "Listen, Jack, don't say anything about my serving you. Della will lose her job if they find out." He nodded toward the back room. Jeff was surprised that there was so little compassion in his voice, only anxiety.

"Nah, we aren't going to say anything," Jack reassured him, looking to Perry for confirmation. Perry nodded.

Joe retrieved two more beers and put them in front of Jack and Perry. "This one's on me," Joe said, then returned to Della.

Jack nodded sagely and whispered, "See what I mean. You do someone a good turn and it comes back to you." He took a long drag on his beer, and then waved to a small, dark-haired woman entering a side door. She shuffled toward them on weary, moccasin-shod feet, carrying a large shoulder bag which, like the load of an inexpertly loaded pack animal, made her list heavily to one side for balance. She wore tight jeans and a lightweight, red sweater that dropped down over her large breasts. At first glance she appeared young, almost teenage, but on looking closer Perry saw soft crow's feet scratched into the corners of her eyes and the beginnings of aging, puffy flesh under her lower lids.

Jack said, "Want something to drink before you go on, Lolita?"

"Yea." Disregarding Jack's encroachment on the chair that had separated him and Perry, she sagged onto the high bar chair between and let her bag slip to the floor. She cocked an eye at Joe and his distraught companion.

Joe stood, but Della grabbed his arm and sat him down again, then used his arm and the table to drag herself up onto unsteady feet. She walked unsteadily behind the bar and started mixing Lolita a drink, spilling some of a premade, fruity-looking liquid onto the counter as she poured. All four people watched as Della set the drink in front of Lolita, then leaned against the counter, her back to all of them, and lit a Parliament cigarette.

Jack turned to Perry and said, "This is my friend, Perry. This little lady is Lolita."

"Nize to meet you Perry," she said, then turning to Jack began talking in a whining, nasal Spanish accent, saying, "I got a gold tonight." She sniffled for emphasis and continued, "And this place is golder inside than it is out." Her Spanish accent and Polynesian features pegged her as Filipino or Puerto Rican. "How'm I goin' to work in here without catchin' pneumonia? I already had walkin' pneumonia once this year."

Jack rested his meaty hand on Lolita's knee and she offered no comment nor made an effort to dislodge it. Perry wondered what Jack's little woman would think of that. And he wondered if this was one of the waitresses here or a musician.

"You know, I'm allergic to everythin' in this damn place. My kid sister, she'll be gradrated next year and I gan be outta here. My sis will have to fen' for herself for once. Maybe I go to San Diego. I'd go back home to Puerto Rico, but you gan't make no livin' there."

Perry felt sorry for the poor woman and put out at Jack who still had a hand on her, but had moved up further on her thigh. This was beginning to be surreal and he wanted to leave. But that wouldn't be very hospitable after Jack had been so nice to him.

Lolita turned to Perry and began complaining about her acting-out adolescent son, as she downed the second fruity drink that the now functioning barmaid, Della, fixed for her without spilling anything. "I tol him I gonna take my fist and smash his pretty face he sasses me again," she concluded. Finished with her second drink, she set down her empty glass and nodded to Della, then asked Joe, "What time we starting?"

"It's getting on toward showtime," Jack said. "The boss lady walked in a while ago so you better move your fanny backstage."

"Honey, tha's all I do here is move my fanny." She made a sour face, and looked at Perry, saying, "Watch my drink, Perry, till I get back or Della will pour it out." She then slid from the seat and walked toward the back, dragging her bag behind her like a dispirited horse pulling a one-bottom plow and disappeared into a recessed door at the end of the bar. Why did she ask me to do that? Perry wondered. What instrument does she play? Or is she a performer of some kind?

As Lolita disappeared, two other women who had been sitting with men at tables stood and followed her. They were of varying heights and weights and had different hair coloring. None of them was particularly attractive though all were curvy. One was dressed in high heels and a knee-length, expensive dress, but the other was dressed much as Lolita had been, in jeans and a nondescript blouse. "Is this an all-women's band?" Perry asked Jack.

A deep belly laugh started somewhere within the cavernous hollow of Jack's oversized girth and spilled out in something of a snort. "Naw, it's a three-man band. They'll come out in a minute or two."

Two young men in their twenties breezed in the front door and sat at the bar, ordered beers, and immediately launched into a discussion of the merits of program buying.

Jack drained his second beer and turned to Perry saying, "You know, I think I'll run on over to the house and bring the little lady over. She'd get a kick out of meeting you and would like the show too. I'll see you in a few minutes." He stood and lumbered out the door leaving Perry to wonder if he really wanted to stay or if he should get up and leave before Jack returned. As he sat pondering this, an old man, black as ebony, emerged from a door at the side of the stage. His body was twisted by some disease or accident. To balance himself he held his left arm out straight and slightly behind his body as he labored across the stage, limping toward an ancient electric organ. Dressed in a black suit of an ancient cut that had been cleaned and pressed, but was threadbare, he paid no heed to the customers. His flowered tie hung to the floor as he stooped and plugged in an archaic speaker, presenting the audience with the black, shiny seat of his worn pants. Like a black-clad interior decorator organizing a furniture arrangement, he moved the small organ this way and that several times until satisfied with its positioning, then he pulled a low, child's-sized chair close to the instrument and sat down with a heavy sigh. His fingers played across the keyboard, testing it, sending out wheezing notes that were unmercifully loud.

The organist had barely settled himself when he was joined by a seedy, white man dressed in a blue woolen sweater and baggy wool pants that must have come from the nearest Salvation Army store. The new arrival took up two drumsticks, beat out a tap-a-ta-tap-tap on the rickety trap, and banged the bass drum and symbols once each. Satisfied that his instrument was still capable of sound, he began an inaudible conversation with his stage mate.

Joe, who'd sat with Della till then, stood, retrieved a saxophone case from the floor, and joined the other two. On stage he opened the case and took out the instrument, fingered the keys, and then put it to his lips, playing a riffle of notes. He was barely seated when, at ten after nine, from the wings, Alfred, the owner, walked to the center of the stage. He now wore slim Italian slippers and had donned an expensively cut suitcoat. The drummer gave a drum roll and the black man struck a rousing note on the organ. In a deep, sonorous voice, the organ player turned to the audience and announced, "Ladies and gentlemen, let me present the pride of Sherry's, our MC, Alfred Conroy."

Alfred held up his hand to stop a wilted crowd response, precious little applause emanating from the yet sparse attendance. He paused, however, as though waiting for a thunderous ovation. The wheezing, ancient organ struck another series of defiant notes before silencing to let Alfred continue.

"Just forget all these empty seats, folks, they're reserved for the New Year's Eve crowd." He paused for effect. "Last New Year's Eve." There was no response from any of the crowd, though the one woman still present in the audience gave a polite smile. It did not escape Alfred, for he addressed the remainder of his spiel directly to her and the small dapper man she sat with.

"No, seriously, we have a crowd of people coming in here in about an hour, in time for our 10:30 show. You want to stay for that show because it's the best. And if that group doesn't get here by then, why, you'll have your own private show." He paused again, expectantly. The woman smiled again.

Clearing his throat Alfred continued, "Well, let's get on with the show. First is Lolita that Latin bombshell from San Juan, where all the girls are beautiful. And here we have her, that tantalizing, Latinizing young lady from San Juan—Lowwwwlitaaa."

When Lolita strutted on to the stage and began to gyrate, it became all too clear to Perry. He had not only been taken for a ride, he'd had been snookered. Cheated. Deceived. Duped into buying what now amounted to at least five drinks which though not yet charged for would likely cost a fortune, probably double what he'd have paid for a cab ride. And would be asked to buy more, he suspected. He started to get up but was arrested by a look from the MC who then addressed him personally.

"You don't want to leave now, sir. I saw Lolita making eyes at you. She'll be disappointed you don't stay to see her dance."

He lowered himself back on to the bar stool and watched.

Lolita walked back and forth on the stage to the accompaniment of Latin music that groaned and sighed from the organ, beat from the drums, and blew from the sax. With her head held high and her eyes on some distant sight beyond the smoke-stained walls, she stared into and through the customers, all who turned their eyes on her. Her breasts stuck out strongly, holding their shape; two Spanish galleons with full sail that flowed through an ocean of sleazy leers. As she slowly uncovered them, one at a time, she massaged those proud vessels through the thick brocaded fandango dress she wore. After they were fully revealed she cupped them again and held them out to everyone for inspection, as if to say, this is the best you will ever feast your eyes on. She moved rhythmically and in time to the gasping and thumping accompaniment of the three-man band. Once during the dance, she caught Perry's eye, smiled and winked, but quickly danced on. He was surprised that she appeared so large and self-assured on the stage, she had so resembled a misbegotten waif when she dragged in a few minutes before complaining of the cold. He was surprised, too, that when she removed her heavy brocaded dress, her small body was muscled as that of a gymnast. She continued gyrating and removing pieces of clothing until she was wearing nothing but a small triangle of cloth over her groin and tassels covering each nipple. Then she exited right stage, followed by enthusiastic applause from the two money-guys and the dapper little man.

Perry knew Jack would not be back with the little woman.

He paid his inflated bill and stood, leaving Lolita's drink to whatever fate decided for it, and headed for the door.

Jack had taken him for a ride.

Fed him devil's meat.

Not edible.

THUMBING IT

My father, Doug Wilkerson, never passed up a hitchhiker. Something about a man standing at the side of the road with his thumb out stirred sympathy in Doug. Like my dad, when I was driving, I was generous to people standing with their thumb out. They were mostly high school and college kids or people down on their luck. Occasionally there were hobos, tramps, and drunks. The summer before going to medical school I was driving my uncle's panel truck from Vernon, Texas, to Altus, Oklahoma, where I was going to hang venetian blinds I'd put together in my uncle's shop. On the back doors of the truck, my uncle, who was also a sign painter, had painted "Caution, blind man at the wheel." The old man who thumbed me to a stop was chuckling when he crawled in the front seat. He smelled strongly of Old Turkey and tobacco; had most likely not seen a bathtub in days.

"Not sure I ought to accept your hospitality," he said. "Ain't ever rode with a blind man before."

Being a good Christian still, I said, "Well, the Lord seems to be guiding me pretty good. Haven't had an accident yet."

"Well, that's good to know. We sure need all the help we can get, now don't we?"

"You a Christian?" We were coming close to the half-mile long bridge over the Red River that separated Texas and Oklahoma when, attempting to be a good, witnessing Christian, I asked him this.

"Yessir, I am. And a Baptist."

"So, you've been baptized and saved?"

"Yessiree." He looked out over the guardrail at the narrow channel of red water winding its way beneath us. "Why, I was baptized right here in the Red River when she was on the rise." He paused. "By John the Baptist."

Though quite dubious of this claim, I talked of faith in the Lord and how it could change one's life. He talked about his weakness for alcohol and we prayed together, though I kept my eyes on the road as we did. With tears in his eyes he swore that he was giving up demon alcohol for good, and I thought that picking up this hitchhiker had, indeed, led to a change in his life. But as we bounced over the railroad tracks at the edge of Altus, the man asked me to pull over. As he readied himself to leave the car, he pulled a fifth of Old Turkey from his jacket pocket.

"I just have to finish off what I got left here in this bottle, then I'm definitely never goin' to have another drink."

My faith in the power of change brought about by witnessing on the open road was sorely shaken. As was my eagerness to pick up hitchhikers.

A PLUMBING ODYSSEY

I am not a plumber.
My niece and nephew, Carol and Larry Barkan, could attest to that fact from one of my previous trip to visit with them in Tempe, Arizona. On that visit, I left them in doubt of my plumbing ability when I installed a Tush-be-Clean in their guest bathroom. A friend of mine, Ross Lathrop, had, years previously, introduced me to this device and it had caught my attention right away, I had to have this Tush-be-Clean, the Japanese answer to a French bidet. The only drawback to the Tush-be-Clean is that it sprays cold water rather than warm, something of a shock on a cold morning. But for a man who spent a good deal of his time growing up on his grandparents' farms, one in eastern Oklahoma and the other in western, that little detail would not be important. The Tush-be-Clean method in western Oklahoma was the outdated Sears catalog, not too bad until all the printed pages were used up and the slick pages had to be used. I never complained of that

too much because I'd also experienced the Tush-be-Clean methods of eastern Oklahoma, with grandparents who didn't get around to building an outhouse. There it was a leaf, bunched-up grass or hay, or, before it became too dried out and hard, a corn cob. Chilly water is next to nothing compared to that.

For reasons I won't go into, I found it so useful that I immediately bought one for each of my three bathrooms. I grew so used to them that when I visited Carol and Larry, I bought two more for their bathrooms so I'd have access to one when I visited. These two wonderful people love not only Carolyn and me, but also any stray dog that wanders by. They had to stop fostering golden retrievers because they found it impossible not to adopt the fostered dogs. They were very tolerant of my coming into their home and installing my Tush-be-Clean. Their tolerance is where the trouble began. But I will get to that in a moment.

First, I want to tell you of the manufacturer's response to my flurry of Tush-be-Clean orders. Shortly after ordering the fifth one, I received a letter from the Tush-be-Clean company naming me the Tush-be-Clean representative for the Chicago metropolitan area. Though amused, I thought it best to write the company and let them know that, despite my flood of orders, I could not accept. "I appreciate your generous offer to appoint me official Tush-be-Clean representative for the Chicago metropolitan area," I wrote. "But please realize that, though 'analyst,' which I am, has 'anal' in its spelling, and the Tush-be-Clean has anal implications, I do not think combining a career as an analyst with that of a Tush-be-Clean representative would be considered very appropriate by many of my patients and colleagues." I did not receive an answer in return. Nonetheless, I am beholden to the company for their product and their willingness to have me as one of their reps. Had they known of my attempts on a visit to my niece to install their equipment, they may not have been so eager for me to represent them. After I had left for home, it was necessary that a bona fide plumber be called in to stop a leak I'd caused during the installation. Rather than fix the leak, he had disconnected my installation.

When in February of the next year, 2012, I came to celebrate my seventy-ninth birthday in Arizona, I was disappointed not to have the Tush-be-Clean hooked to the toilet. It was a minor inconvenience, to be sure, but I found its absence disappointing. However, I had no intention on this visit to again have a plumbing tool in my hand. I was there to visit, finish reading *A Most Dangerous Method: The Story of Jung, Freud, and Sabina Spielrein*, to write the last chapter of my memoir, and to relax. Little did I know what was in store for me from the plumbing device my old friend Ross Lathrop had introduced me to.

For the first week I relaxed with my wife Carolyn and my son Bruce, who was visiting the Phoenix area for the first time. We enjoyed country-western dancing, eating out in fancy restaurants, going to a lecture by a Jewish, lesbian writer, Fran Lebowitz, and hiking in the Botanical Garden and the Superstition Mountains. (I should mention that Bruce and I went hiking in the Superstitions alone; Larry, my nephew, will no longer go into the wilderness with me because I'd once taken him out and gotten us lost for a few hours before being rescued by a lone hiker who seemed to have materialized from out of the very rocks along the creek bed we were traversing. It may not have actually been that half-hour we were lost as much as the three hours I had little idea where we were that made him come to the decision not to trust walking among the cacti except for the well-marked paths of the Botanical Garden.)

My son Bruce became engrossed with taking pictures of his own and my shadow as they fell against a canvas of rock, water, and vegetation. He came up with some very interesting photos that appeared on rocks as if they were the figures once drawn by Native Americans. One had to wonder if shadows were the inspiration for that earlier rock art.

After our three-and-a-half-hour sojourn in the Superstition Mountains, Bruce and I stopped in Goldfield, the old mining town four-and-a-half miles east of Apache Junction, where we sat in the saloon and were entertained by a yodeling Paula Williamson, who was touted by her companion, dressed as John Wayne, as someone the Western Music Association had named three times the Yodeling Champion. It so inspired me that I began to practice my rusty yodeling skills. From the time I was a twelve-year-old and would give a yodel-like call to summon my collie, Lad, I practiced yodeling from time to time, mostly in the shower, and eventually learned to give a passable yodel. It came in handy on a visit to Switzerland in 1981.

Carolyn and I had stayed for three nights in a small village just below Piz Gloria, the revolving restaurant on top of the Schilthorn in the Bernese Oberland that was made famous in the James Bond movie, *On Her Majesty's Secret Service*. As I was to take the cable car down to my own vehicle so I could leave for France, Carolyn and I were feeling disappointed that we'd been in Switzerland for five days and she'd not seen Heidi and I'd not once heard a yodel. Determined not to leave the mountains behind me without hearing at least one yodel, even if it was my own, I stepped into a small room where the cable car was waiting, but that was momentarily empty. I let loose with my best yodel. I almost fell off the mountain when I heard, in three-part harmony, an answering yodel from the next room. I yodeled again. Again, I received an answer. The hair stood up on the back of my neck and for a fleeting second, I wondered if the mountains were haunted by long dead yodelers. No, it was a trio of professional yodelers who had come to the village for a concert, which I had missed, and were traveling down the mountain with us. They yodeled for all the fifteen minutes or so we traveled down, and then, as I walked to my car that was parked three or four blocks from the hotel they adjourned to, I would yodel. They would answer. I left Switzerland fully satisfied with my visit. A disappointed Carolyn never laid eyes on Heidi. Now, thirty years later with the Superstition Mountains only three miles away, I decided to let go a yodel. To my disappointment, Paula Williamson did not answer.

Nevertheless, back in my niece's and nephew's home, I began to occasionally let go a practice yodel, trying to get back in form. My son and nephew weren't too impressed, and my niece only slightly indulgent. But each time I let go with a yodel, my niece's and nephew's dog, Becca, a twelve-year-old golden retriever, would struggle to her feet and hurry to me, her tail wagging and her eyes bright. It was gratifying that at least one living creature there in the house had a positive response to my efforts. But I digress.

Though distracted by all these other activities, I was, from the beginning of that first week's visit, nagged by the disappointment that the Tush-be-Clean I'd previous installed on their guest room toilet had gone missing. I felt pushed to play plumber again and my Tush-be-Clean odyssey was destined to begin.

Bruce flew back to France after six days, but Carolyn and I had another ten days of vacation. Though still busy going out to eat, working out at LA Fitness, baking two pear pies, (actually the only pies I'd ever baked) and visiting with Jeni Buckholtz and Linda and John Artec, I decided to, after all, attack the problem of the bathroom's installation, which I assumed would be effortless because installing my own Tush-be-Clean had been so easy.

Sometime before the advent of the Tush-be-Cleans and the new bathroom in my house, I had occasion to learn something of the intricacies of the toilet tank mechanism. My friend Ross was married to a very enterprising woman who had two jobs going at the same time, one of them hostessing a B&B from out of her large, five-bedroom house that had finally disgorged four, mostly grown young daughters, leaving four rooms sitting like empty vacuums. Carol Lathrop could not stand vacuums, so she filled the rooms with paying clients, many of whom became so regular in attendance that they became friends who, when she was full, would not be turned away without Carol Lathrop doing all she could to find accommodations for them. Once, as a favor to her, we agreed to keep a family of four over Saturday and Sunday night. No sooner had they unpacked their bags than they tried our new bathroom, all done in white and blue and arguably the most attractive room in our one-hundred-year-old house. Down the stairs came the father, a professor of biology, who informed me the toilet did not flush.

Sure enough, he was right. I don't think he was too impressed when I brought up a bucket of water and, dumping it in the bowl, cleared it. I was sure the prospect of spending the weekend endlessly filling a bucket did not appeal to him, so I assured him I would call a plumber to see to the toilet while he and his family were out to lunch.

Silly me. Have you ever tried to get a plumber out on a Saturday afternoon? Even if you know you'll pay double? I did. And with no luck. "Monday, buddy. That's the best I can do unless it's a real emergency. Don't sound like it's down to that, yet, you turnin' off the water and having a bucket and all that." It had been a mistake to give him too much information.

Now I had been quite handy throughout my life, having taken apart a furnace, repairing and then reassembling it; completely rewiring my house when an electrician had taken one look and flatly told me he wouldn't even walk in my door for less than a king's ransom; having downed and cut into pieces twenty- and thirty-foot-high trees; installed washers and dryers; and replaced faulty door knobs and locks. I had been willing to play at being a furnace repairman, an electrician, a locksmith, and a tree removal service, but never had

A PLUMBING ODYSSEY

I considered playing at being a plumber. It seemed so, I don't know, kind of a muck-ruck sort of task. But now I was stuck.

With not a little aggravation, I lifted the lid from the tank and peered inside. I fiddled with the mechanism, jiggled this and rattled that, only to find that a little water would flow when I messed with the thing-a-ma-jig and nothing would happen when I rattled the other do-hickies.

So it was off to the hardware store where a knowledgeable clerk listened to my description of what I'd found, tried not to snicker, and then presented to me all the steps of removing the old ballcock, or thing-a-ma-jig, then assembling, and installing the new. My guests were quite impressed that I'd managed to get a plumber to come out and fix the toilet in a matter of two hours. They were never told I was that plumber. Perhaps it was that experience that led to my belief I could do my own Tush-be-Clean installations.

When it had come time to install the first Tush-be-Cleans in my own home, I'd approached the chore with some confidence that it would be no big deal. I was rewarded with an easy task well done. Therefore, I had not been prepared for the difficulties met in the bathroom belonging to Larry and Carol. That effort having ended in a leaky installation; necessitating a real plumber to be called in was, as I've revealed, disappointing. He'd said the ballcock seal was compromised and the Tush-be-Clean's female connection to the ballcock was missing a cone washer, which was the correct one needed. My niece was very kind about the trouble I'd caused her, and I know how troublesome a guest can be sometimes, even the most well-meaning ones. That made me hesitate playing at being a plumber once more. I did not want to again be a nuisance to my hosts as I'd at one time experienced with a guest.

I once had an overnight visit by a plumber's wife, the daughter of a neighbor who hadn't enough room to put up all his children and grandchildren for Christmas night, and asked if I would do him a favor and have her and his two granddaughters spend the night in my two empty, third-floor bedrooms. I did so happily.

Not so happy when I noticed running down my stairwell walls a cascade of water and then heard the anguished cry of my adult guest. I was second on the scene, my wife having preceded me and wisely, or I should say, knowledgably, turned off the supply stop valve located behind the toilet, interfering with the cheerful overflow that had begun minutes earlier. Fortunately, the toilet had flushed its contents before its stubborn refusal to stop running. My plumber's wife guest did not even know there was a small knob behind the toilet bowl, and that turning it would staunch the gushing torrent of water.

She was hysterical. "I've ruined your bathroom," she wailed. "I'm a plumber's wife and I didn't know how to turn the water valve off!" She was in tears that did not stop until I assured her it was difficult to ruin an entire bathroom with a little, well a lot, of clean water. I also said, "As for the ruined bathroom carpet and the tile that pulled up from the floor, not to worry; Carolyn has wanted a new bathroom for the last five years and now we have a very good reason to move ahead."

After a few more tears and "I'm so sorry" a dozen times, she calmed down and helped clean up the mess. My wife was actually pleased and did get a new bathroom put in. I didn't help with that.

So, when I was visiting Larry and Carol and was faced with wishing for a Tush-be-Clean. I didn't want to call a plumber in for a task I should be able to accomplish. From those previous installations in my home and in my niece's, I knew where the water connection to the toilet bowl was, that a 7/8-inch IPS straight thread fits toilet connections, and I also knew what a flexible water connector is. I could ask for a female pipe swivel connection or a male iron pipe connection without calling them thing-a-ma-jigs while my cheeks reddened with embarassment.

I also knew how tight a fit it is behind and beneath said bowl; I'd had experience.

So, even though I'd first decided I did not want to do any plumbing on this visit, I tackled the job once more. It was a solitary job; my nephew, a very articulate, smart, personable, and knowledgeable fellow, would be of little help. If I sent him for something like a Phillips screwdriver, he'd give me a blank look. While I tackled the Tush-be-Clean job, he chose to watch the likes of *The Daily Show* and *The Colbert Report*; which, in part, explains why he is more knowledgeable than I am about current events. Carol, my sweet, loving niece who pampers my wife and me when we visit, though willing to help, would likely be made anxious by the dismemberment of her toilet by a relatively unskilled nonplumber. I don't ask either one for assistance.

First, I went to the hardware store to purchase a cone washer. I was shown several, none which were the correct 7/8-inch size. I settled on a 15/16-inch one, dismantled the water supply, and installed the Tush-be-Clean hardware, not an easy task lying on the floor and reaching behind the toilet bowl with a Vise-Grip.

Everything in place, I turned the water valve on and was rewarded by a squirt in the face. The female attachment to the ballcock male end was too deep and would not snug up sufficiently. Thinking for a moment of Freud and Jung, I wondered if either of them had ever held a wrench. I doubted it; they spent their vacations in lovely Swiss or Austrian mountains thinking deep thoughts and writing philosophical and psychological treatises.

Installation had stalled, so I took off the rest of the day to attend the local art museum to see an exhibit of Frank Lloyd Wright's architectural drawings. A few days later I would take a tour of his winter home and architectural school in the middle of a large patch of cactus-infested desert. New students were, and still are fifty-three years after Wright's death, required to live in tents on the grounds while they create their own living quarters. Except for the men's and women's bathrooms constructed specifically for visitors to the gift shop, not once were we shown a bathroom on the premises. I had to wonder if those poor souls who came to study had to resort to the same behavior as I did back on my grandfather Wilkerson's farm and, if so, where they found the grass or leaves. All I could see were prickly cacti and small-leafed trees.

Next day, I drove back to the hardware store to find a washer that would take up the slack in the female end of the Tush-be-Clean. No luck. All the spacer washers in the more than eighty bins of washers in stock were 1/16-inch off. Trying to be helpful, the clerk suggested I try the swimming pool company down the block. "They have some strange sizes there," he said.

Again, no luck. The pool company clerk sent me on to Lowes, a large outlet store that the clerk assured had, "Just about anything you can think of." Off I drove a mile and a half only to find that Lowes had fewer bins of the wrong-sized washers than the hardware store. It would take a plumber, after all, to install my Tush-be-Clean. Disconsolate, I prepared to leave. But as I was walking to the exit, a clerk, an attractive blond woman of about 45 years wearing a thin, red, cotton jacket bearing the Lowes logo, called out to me, "You find what you needed, sir?"

"Afraid not."

"That's too bad. What was it you were looking for?"

I told her of my search for the 7/8-inch washer and she gave me a big smile. "That sounds like the size of a garden hose washer. Come over here and let's see." She led me to shelves stacked with garden supplies, retrieved a small packet of yellow washers, and handed it to me. They fit the Tush-be-Clean's female end perfectly.

"You're a life saver," I said.

In the flush of good feelings that finding the correct-sized washer had engendered, we chatted a bit before I commented about the size of

A PLUMBING ODYSSEY

the store and her being isolated amid gardening tools, which did not seem to be attracting many customers. That led to her mentioning it was her lunch hour and that she would be leaving soon to drive to a nearby restaurant, or maybe home, for her hour break. The atmosphere became a bit charged then, as I realized she had offered an opening for me to ask her to lunch. I can't say there wasn't a flash of desire to do just that, but then, given I was at least thirty years her senior, a married man, and a man with a job to do, I disregarded the siren call of the young woman and backed off.

I may have imagined the disappointed look she gave me before she smiled and said, "If you ever have any needs, come back to Lowes."

"Thanks," I said as I walked away, "Next time I have a need, I'll certainly come here." My face was still burning five minutes later from the unintended double entendre, a slip of my untrustworthy unconscious.

It reminded me of another time I wore my unconscious on my sleeve at a wedding I'd once attended where I found myself in conversation with cousins of the groom, one in particular, a psychiatrist, about her daughter who lived in Saudi Arabia and would not come home to visit. A mountain of a woman weighing four hundred pounds if an ounce, she was not too well-liked by most of the family and it did not take long for me to understand why: she was arrogant and pushy, and very hateful of her daughter's failure to come home, thus forcing her poor old mother to make the long trip overseas.

"Well," I said without thinking, "you know what they say in Saudi Arabia, don't you? If you can't bring Mohammed to the mountain, you bring the mountain to Mohammed."

The mountain glared at me before I realized what I'd blurted out. I fled. But by that slip of the old unconscious, when it became known to them, I became a hero of the family. Driving away from the Lowes store, I was happy no one had heard my unconscious breaking through and showing itself in my suggestive rejoinder to the attractive clerk.

Arriving back at my nieces' home with renewed optimism, I pushed two garden hose washers into place and, lying prone once more with Vise-Grip in hand, attached the female end of the Tush-be-Clean to its male extension and turned the water valve, hoping against hope the installation was finished. No water sprayed in my face. Success!

A few minutes later, as I sat typing the finishing pages to my memoir, I heard a shushing sound that I assumed was from the tap in the sink. I paid it no heed. But, then, thinking my wife might have left the tap running when she had been there moments before, I rose to look. The sink taps were off, but I realized I was sloshing through water. On the floor lay the Tush-be-Clean's spray head unattached from the hose. Water was shooting straight out at my shoe. My shirt sleeve and pants cuff were splashed as I reached behind the toilet bowl and turned off the water. Examining the spray head, I found that its female end had cracked.

By the time I'd mopped up all the water on the floor, and changed out of my damp clothes, I was about ready to give up, but remembered the second Tush-be-Clean kit I'd never installed. Taking it down from the shelf, I took the new hose and substituted it for the cracked one, which meant getting back down on the floor again with my wrench.

Two days after I finished the job there was no flooding. I held my breath. And I was not about to order, and install a Tush-be-Clean in my niece's other bathroom. Nor did I intend to go out and buy the latest version of a bidet introduced to me by Larry's and Carol's friend now living in the Sagewood retirement home, though its installation seems less complex than that of the Tush-be-Clean. It is remote controlled, with tepid, warm, and warmer settings as well as women's front or back and men's back water flow. It warms the toilet seat before use. It was too intimidating for Larry to use, so it would not be worth my while to attack that project.

A PLUMBING ODYSSEY

Before arriving at the retirement home, we had stopped at the nearby Musical Instrument Museum where we saw every conceivable instrument thought up and played by men and women from every imaginable part of the world. Scores and scores of drums, whistles, flutes, bow and string instruments, and horns adorned the walls. They were of all sizes and shapes, the smallest being the prototype of a violin that was six inches long, all the way to a bass fiddle that was over nine feet tall and required a stepstool and special levers for the upper reaches of the strings. It occurred to me that I'd only seen four versions of a bidet, and I wondered at the lack of ingenuity man devoted to that end. "Music is for the soul," the introductory video intoned. I think now I should have responded, "Yes, but Tush-be-Cleans are more practical."

When I headed home to Chicago and back to my real profession, I hoped to visit again the following March. Of course, if the present installation goes bad, I may be politely asked not to return. But I hope Carol and Larry do realize that things can go wrong. After all, I am not a plumber.

BREAKNECK SPEED

When my father was in his midfifties, he made the decision to stop driving so fast—to become more careful—to give up the thrill of driving at breakneck speed. When I went to visit him a few years later, he was lying in a hospital bed with weights attached to his feet and a metal plate screwed into the top of his cranium, stretching him out like a medieval victim on a torture rack. In pain but quite conscious he told me: "I drove fast all my life and when I slowed down, the sons-of-a-bitches caught up with me."

A fourteen-wheeler had run into the back of his car—there's some dispute in the family as to what he was driving at the time—and flipped it over into a ditch. He came out alive but with a broken neck.

I thought of that visit while I lay on my back in Northwestern Hospital's ICU with my own broken neck. Watching my father lying in pain and suffering back then, I had no idea that I'd suffer a similar fate in my eighty-fourth year.

The year 2017 did not end well for me. November 18 began happily enough. The Yachnin family and I all walked the three blocks from my apartment to the Christkindl market at Daley Plaza, where we drank hot-mulled cider or hot chocolate and I bought a bag of chocolate candies filled with pear liquor, which I had done every Christmas for three years. We strolled among booths selling Christmas nutcrackers, Christmas tree ornaments, cuckoo clocks, beer steins, jewelry, clothes, wooden handicrafts, and toys for all ages. I bought Emma, Luke, and Josh each a small Christmas gift as we walked around in the rain. I should have bought myself one of the Christmas nutcrackers, the German symbol of good luck, protectors of the home and guards against evil spirits. I would soon need some good luck.

Before leaving the market, we all trooped into a large, common dining room filled with parents and their children. It smelled of crepes, sausages, potato pancakes, strudel, and sweet, hot pastries. Melinda and I made a short excursion to a booth that sold steaming hot crepes which we brought back to our hungry companions. Finished, we headed for my parking garage, stopping at a special doughnut shop where I shared with Melinda an oversize circle of cake dough slathered in sugar frosting and drowned in sprinkles. Stuffed, we walked on; it was home-again-home-again time for the Yachnins. I walked them to my elevators and rode to the fifth floor there to escort them down the inclined concrete drive to their car. As we pushed through the heavy door into the parking area, exuberant, eleven-year-old Josh took off running.

For God knows what reason, I went racing after him, determined to beat him to the car. As we raced pell-mell down the inclined cement drive, I lost my forward balance and took a nosedive toward the concrete. There was a moment of disbelief and an even briefer moment of realization that I was headed, no pun intended, for a hard landing. I instinctively tried breaking my fall with an old judo maneuver

I'd learned forty-eight years before, one that always worked on the forgiving tatami mats of a martial arts studio. The idea is to make an arc of the right arm, tuck the head and roll down the arm and onto the arched back, letting momentum carry the body back forward and allow one to come to rest on two feet. Didn't work for me. Broke two fingers instead. Landed like a bowling ball on my head and face. Broke my nose. Broke three vertebrae. Gashed my forehead and bled like a stuck hog.

I rolled onto my back and, though conscious, I didn't immediately want to get up, which was a good thing. I had no idea at the time, around 3:30 P.M., but to stand would have been disastrous, as I had no support left for my spinal cord. When the Yachnins gathered around and said they were going to call an ambulance, I argued that I could very well ride to the hospital in the back of a car. My friends had the foresight to insist I lie still with my broken nose against the unforgiving cement smelling of motor oil and tire treads for the time it took them to call an ambulance and for it to arrive.

I remember arguing with my friends, I remember being lifted onto a stretcher and loaded into the back of an ambulance. I remember apologizing for making jokes. "I handle my anxiety that way," I told one of the medics. And that's all I remember until I woke up in the ICU thirty-six hours or so later. My son, Scott, who was with me within an hour of my fall, said I was responsive for the first several hours in the ER and was answering questions and agreeing to recommendations made by the physicians. "When they told you that they needed to operate on your neck and stabilize your spine, I was reminded, by your response, of a war movie where the soldier is told he must face extraordinary odds and he, locked-and-loaded, says, 'Let's get on with it.'"

I don't remember having to lie in the ER for a long time because the gash in my forehead and lip had bled profusely and the doctors were concerned that my being on a blood thinner, combined with the hard knock to my head, could result in a bleed into my brain. The plastic surgeon who was on call stitched up my lip and forehead wounds without my remembering it. My effort to play at being a judoka and break my fall had led to a disjointed and broken ring finger and a broken little finger. Someone taped them together. There was nothing to be done about my broken nose but stop the bleeding.

It took them a while to read the X-ray and CT scan images of my neck and see that three of my cervical vertebrae were shattered. There was absolutely nothing supporting my spinal column. My cervical vertebrae were a mess. I lay there with bone fragments within a fraction of a centimeter from severely injuring my spinal cord. The sixth cervical vertebrae had sustained what is called a tear-drop fracture which in 1988 was described in an article by physicians at Northwestern Hospital, the very one to where I was taken after my injury. They wrote:

> *The flexion teardrop fracture (FTDF) is a common injury of the cervical spine that often has a devastating outcome [1–3] . . . The lesion is also characterized by complete disruption of both the anterior and posterior ligamentous structures, resulting in marked instability at the site of injury [4]. The characteristic neurologic injury accompanying the FTDF is the anterior cord syndrome. This syndrome consists of quadriplegia with loss of pain, temperature, and touch sensations, and preservation of the posterior column senses of position, motion, and vibration [1, 4]. Neurologic consequences are usually severe with the FTDF; however, in some cases there are incomplete deficits or even intact neurologic status [2, 5].*

Luckily, I had thus far avoided immediate injury to the cord. At ten that evening, when Dr. Smith, the neurosurgeon, took one look at the images of my neck, he saw that, like Humpty Dumpty, I'd "had a great fall." He wasted no time putting me on the table where, thirty minutes later he and his assistants spent the next seven hours, from 10:30 P.M. until 4:30 A.M., strengthening my cervical spine with two titanium rods and any number of screws. Unlike Humpty-Dumpty I was put "back together again." Fortunately, it was Dr. Smith and his assistants, not all the king's horses and all the king's men, who attempted, and succeeded, in the repair. Sometime after four thirty I was transferred to the ICU.

In the middle of the morning, I emerged from out of my drug-induced stupor frantic with anxiety and fighting the endotracheal tube, so they put me under again for another twenty-four hours. I don't remember this, but Jennifer, my daughter-in-law, said that, when I awoke a second time there was a look of pure terror on my face. What I do recall, though, is the feeling of extreme relief when the tube slithered out of my throat. When I became fully aware of my surroundings, there was Scott, a guardian angel, leaning over me and smiling. The next thing I noticed was a plastic neck brace holding me rigidly in place and reminding me of Scott's replica of a sixteenth-century gorget that he once donned with his full set of metal armor in preparation for battle during the Society of Creative Anachronism's Pensic Wars. My battle I came to find out was to tolerate the restricted movement this instrument of tortuous protection demanded.

Scott was with me for most, if not all, of the first three days of the ordeal. At some point, I don't remember when, I gave him the names of all the people who needed to know I would not be keeping my appointments: doctors, dentists, dance instructors, friends and relatives—my coteacher of the case history writing seminar we were conducting. He called them and then started posting news of my progress on Facebook and friending anyone who wanted to follow it. He took off time from work as a public school teacher to be with me.

My friends Carol Lathrop and Melinda Yachnin each spent a night sitting by my bed. Carol Barkan, my Arizona niece, came and spent six days and nights, much of it at my bedside. Jennifer, my daughter-in-law, arranged for round-the-clock care after my niece had to return to Arizona. My son Bruce called several times to talk with me and ask about my progress. Friends and colleagues started dropping in to visit or sending flowers and gifts. The office of the building I live in dropped off three balloons on my first day in ICU, one, in the form of a can of Campbell's chicken soup, was the hit of the ward. A colleague brought me three pairs of bright Christmas socks that everyone in PT admired. The Child and Adolescent Analysis committee, the Candidates' Association of the Chicago Institute for Psychoanalysis, and the members of my study group all sent flowers or candy or both. One couple, the husband who, like me, was in childhood, an avid Tarzan fan, brought me Tarzan movies, discs, and a graphic Tarzan novel. I felt remembered and cared for and came to fully realize what a loving and caring circle of people there was in my life. And I needed them, for all my troubles did not end with neck surgery.

A blood clot that had formed between my spine and esophagus blocked any effort on my part to swallow. To offset this, two young physicians came into my room on the second evening and attempted to insert a nasal catheter into my stomach. Seven times they prodded the back of my throat, three of those times gaining access to my trachea which left me tearing, choking, and coughing. After the seventh try, they gave up and revealed that most people would tolerate attempts to intubate them only two or three times. They thanked me for my patience but I could only nod my insincere, "You're welcome." So, for the twelve days I was in the ICU I was fed intravenously. Neither food nor drink passed my lips. I lost twelve pounds, and though prior to my injury I'd wanted to lose a few inches to take pressure off my waistline, I became quite aware that fasting while lying in bed partially encased in body armor was not a good weight-loss regimen. Then there were the two blood clots discovered in my lungs.

Two young doctors—they seemed to mostly come in pairs and they all seemed too young to really be physicians—approached my bed the day after I regained consciousness in the ICU and explained that it was possible that more clots originating in my legs would form and break loose to wreak havoc with my lungs. Not good! I knew before they told me that more clots could worsen my already abnormal heart rhythm. Part of my lung might die. I could develop pulmonary hypertension which would lead to shortness of breath with activity—there would go my dancing—chest pain and angina and heart failure—there would go most other physical activity. If a large clot blocked the main artery to my lungs, blood flow could be completely interrupted, causing cardiac arrest and sudden death. There would go everything. In other words, I was at risk and they recommended that I allow the surgeons to insert a filter into my venae cavae, the large vein carrying blood back to the lungs. No-brainer. Lock and load. Go for it. I'd survived sans-nothing thus far and wanted no part of further clots in the lung that could finish me off. Two hours later, still groggy from light anesthesia and with a sore neck where they'd cut their way into my internal jugular vein to thread the filter all the way down to my abdominal cavity and into my inferior venae cavae, I found myself back in my room, hopefully safe from further clots. For the most part, that was the end of procedures for the time being, though there were other minor irritants.

I had experienced atrial fibrillation preceding my injury and that condition was rightly seen as a complicating factor in my care, and it worried my cardiologist and aggravated me. It couldn't be immediately brought under control because the drug, Multaq, which I'd been taking to control it, could not be given intravenously, only by mouth. And I couldn't swallow. I was going in and out of AFib episodes all day long. They gave me instead a drug I'd refused several months ago because of its potential to destroy the liver or kidneys. I don't know how many doses I was given before being able to once again swallow the Multaq but I do know my liver and kidneys still function so it couldn't have been too long.

I noticed an interesting phenomenon in regards to my atrial fib. When my friend, Melinda Yachnin, who was with me when I had the accident, was visiting me in the hospital she happened to mention the word doughnuts and I immediately went into a brief episode of atrial fibrillation. This happened two more times while she was with me! I'd had that wonderfully sinful, sprinkles-doused doughnut only minutes prior to having my accident and apparently the association of the doughnut to my accident would send my heart racing. I told Melinda she had to avoid the word. I did not use it either in the days to come as I lay waiting for PT to begin.

My trips to PT began after I was able to get out of bed for short periods of time and sit in a chair. Blessed relief getting off my back. From there it was trips to the bathroom and then short walks down the hall and back with a safety belt fastened around my waist and clutched tightly in the hand of a nurse or other caretaker. They did not want me to fall again.

A speech therapist visited me on the fourth or fifth day in the ICU and she instituted a course of exercises that would strengthen my swallowing response. Who would ever think that swallowing while you press your tongue between your front teeth could be helpful to someone whose swallowing reflex had been traumatized by attempts to put a tube into their stomach? Or tightening the muscles at the back of the throat while not swallowing? Or forcefully swallowing? And doing each exercise thirty times.

After the first week of gradual exercise I was taken to the physiotherapy floor where I was asked to walk straight lines, weave in and out of objects on the floor, walk backward. I then graduated to walking a low balance beam and further distances, though always with the safety belt. After three or four days of this, I grew bored and suggested to one of the female physical therapists that we dance instead, that dancing would help with balance and stamina just as well. At first, she demurred, claiming she didn't know how to dance. I responded that I would teach her a dance step, and she was a good enough sport that she allowed me to show her a basic waltz step. Thereafter, though each day I had a different therapist, I taught a new dance step, Argentine tango, foxtrot, east coast swing, cha-cha, and rhumba. All the young therapists were quite good-natured and some were potentially pretty good dancers. It was an excellent way to begin to develop new balance skills which my altered neck movement compromised somewhat, though less so than I'd been worried would happen.

By the end of the second week I could swallow without half of what was going down invading my trachea, so they told me I could now eat soft foods and I was ecstatic until they brought my first meal. Everything tasted as if it had been doused in sugar. Scrambled eggs, toast, butter, meat—absolutely everything. I did not know at the time that it would take a month for food to once again seem appetizing. The ability to swallow also allowed me to take my Multaq and the AFib episodes decreased remarkably, so they sent me to the Rehab floor.

Fortunately, my rather excellent physicality, for a man of my age, from dancing three to five times a week and exercising daily before the accident, accelerated my recovery and I was allowed to go home just one week after I entered rehab. Encased in my plastic garget, I walked into my home on December 8, 2017. It was gratifying to me that my son, Scott, stayed with me the first few days I was at home, and that my wonderful family, friends, and colleagues visited and gave me attention as well. On their first visit to me in the IC unit, the neurosurgery residents had told me I would have to wear a neck brace for three to six months during which time I could not fly or travel. A planned trip to Santa Fe with my son, daughter-in-law, and her family for the Christmas holidays had to be canceled. Scott volunteered to stay in Chicago with me, but I refused to have him miss the holiday and insisted he go. I was by then perfectly able to take care of myself.

Gradually resuming many of my usual activities, I looked forward to regaining most if not all my energy and physicality. Unable to imagine dancing wearing a full neck brace, I stayed away from the ballrooms, but walked on the treadmill and did all the exercises taught me in rehab. And, as my taste buds began to more and more recognize that everything entering my mouth was not doused with sugar, I ate. And ate. And ate. While in the hospital, I had lost twelve pounds but quickly gained back six. I hoped that would be the extent of what I gained even as I began enjoying the taste of sugar once more and dug in to all the candies and other goodies I'd received over the holidays and while in the hospital. And would gain another six before I quit eating so much.

Six weeks after I nosedived into the concrete drive, I had X-rays of my neck taken and then saw the neurosurgeon who had operated on my neck. He asked how I was doing, and then he excused himself to examine my X-rays. He told me the X-rays showed I was healing well, that the bone was filling in nicely, and that he was pleased with my progress. I had half a dozen questions to ask but, before I could formulate them, he shook my hand and walked out of the room. I think we'd spent all of three or four minutes together—total. Sitting there rather frustrated, I was surprised when he stuck his head back in the door and said, "By the way, you don't have to wear the neck brace anymore."

"What did you say?" I asked incredulously.

"You can throw the neck brace away. You don't need it anymore."

I was ecstatic. I threw it away that very day.

As soon as I threw the brace away, I resumed dancing the three types of dancing I loved, American Style Ballroom, International Style Ballroom, and Argentine Tango, and though my stamina had diminished considerably, I was able to dance well. The aches and pains in my neck, shoulders, back, and legs were pretty constant, but I figured they were the price one paid for sustaining a broken neck.

I had always wondered about the term "breakneck speed." Now that I knew how fast that was, I made a New Year's resolution to never again race eleven-year-old boys down concrete drives. Other than that, I've invoked few restrictions on my eighty-six-year-old self, other than those dictated by extreme exhaustion.

DON'T BE FOOLISH, OLD MAN

She was dressed in a midcalf length skirt and short-sleeved top that exposed warm, olive-skinned arms and bare shoulders. Shapely calves. The flip-flops showed her fine toes, the nails painted the same as her fingernails in a cool summer green. Fine figured, I couldn't help glancing as I entered the service area of the Conoco station on South Harlem. Turning to me as if eyes in the back of her head had noticed my quick glance, her generous mouth turned up at the corners and she walked up to me. Her soft brown eyes sparkled with what looked to be recognition as she said, "Hello. Remember me?"

I must have given her a comical if not blank stare because a soft chuckle erupted from the back of her throat. "You remember. I'm Sandra. The woman with the two daughters. You used to come into the bank where I worked and we talked about them."

I remembered another Latino woman who worked at the MB Financial bank I frequented for years, but this was not her and no other came to mind, though I racked that aging organ looking for an image. It embarrassed me that I could not remember such an attractive and outgoing person. "I'm really sorry," I said. "I just can't seem to remember. You'll have to forgive me."

"Well, it's been a long time and I was away for most of it. I took my daughters to California and I only moved back recently. I'm staying with my cousin." She motioned in the direction of a rather unattractive, heavyset woman standing at the cashier's window. She nodded to me and gave a friendly wave.

"This is really weird. I can't come up with a single memory."

"It doesn't matter." Her full lips parted, showing perfect teeth—and a perfect smile.

"It matters to me. I hate it when I can't remember someone that remembers me."

"Hey. I said it didn't matter. But how have you been doing?"

"Okay, I guess. No complaints. At least none you'd like to hear."

"Oh, I don't know about that. Why don't we get together for coffee sometime? Catch up. Tell me what's really going on in your life."

"I don't get out to this area often," I said.

"Oh. You don't live out here anymore?"

"I never did. I live downtown, now." It dawned on me that she may not have been referring to my Chicago bank. "You were talking about a bank out here, weren't you?"

"Yes. I thought I'd seen you out here in the bank I used to work in. Guess I was mistaken. So why are you way out here?"

"I occasionally drive out to Glendora for an afternoon of dancing."

"Oh? You dance? I love to dance salsa."

"I do ballroom dancing. I've never learned to salsa." She placed a soft, warm palm in mine. "Maybe you could teach me to do ballroom dancing. I'd really like to go dancing with you."

DON'T BE FOOLISH, OLD MAN

It finally dawned on me that this young woman, however young she was, was making a pretty determined pass at me. She was every adolescents' most cherished fantasy, that a beautiful woman, a stranger, would come and throw herself at them. I was flattered. Maybe she did admire me somewhat. I was well dressed: I had on my dark blue denim pants and light blue linen jacket I'd bought in Buenos Aries. I was fit and trim. Maybe even looked distinguished. For an eighty-five-year-old man I didn't look too decrepit. There are a great number of women who like to dance with me but they were all past sixty. And only want to dance. This woman was signaling she wanted something more. But from me? Why me? I thought about looking in the mirror that morning and seeing myself.

No adolescent there.
Not a man in his prime.
Not a man of middle age.
Not even an older man.
I saw a very old man.

Concluding that Sandra was after something that would more likely lead to me being scammed, I became appropriately suspicious. Over the years I'd had innumerable incidents in downtown Chicago with scammers, three who had used much the same opening gambit as Sandra. The first had been years ago as I was climbing the stairs of the Grant Park parking garage and upon reaching the top was greeted by a man of color dressed in jeans and a solid blue shirt. His shoes weren't shined but they weren't broken down or scuffed badly. He looked directly at me with good eye contact and said, "I know you."

"You do?" I said, surprised by his comment, but still taking the work-roughened hand he held out and returning the firm handshake.

"You don't remember me?"

"No," I said. "I'm sorry I don't."

"You know, I used to be one of the maintenance men for your building."

"At 55 North Michigan?"

"Yea. 55 North Michigan. You remember now? I was there two years ago. I had to leave to go take care of my mom. She fell and broke her hip and then had complications."

I shook my head as if to clear it or shake the cobwebs away. "I'm really sorry about your mother. And that I can't recall you."

"Well, that's okay. I remember you really well. You used to be so friendly. Always said hello. You weren't like some of those others in the building who'd look right through me like I wasn't there."

That sounded like me, I hoped. I wouldn't want to be known as someone who treated the working people in the building as if they didn't exist. "That's kind of you to say."

"Wasn't there something about your kid you told me? I can't exactly remember."

"Was it about my son here or the one in France?"

"Yea. That was it. You told me all about your son living in France. How's he doing?"

I was totally flummoxed at this point. If I'd told him about my son, I must have talked to him at length at some point. "He's doing well. He's on holiday now down south near Toulon until he starts teaching school again this fall."

"And the boy here in Chicago?"

"He's a teacher as well and on holiday for the summer."

"Well, that's real good, having two teachers in the family."

"Yes, it is. Thanks," I said and then added, "I've got to get on to work now. It was nice talking to you." I started walking away. I had a patient to see.

He fell in beside me, saying nothing more until we reached the corner of Washington and Michigan Avenue and we had to pause for the light to turn green. As we stood there he said, "You know, I've had some rough times since I left my job to take care of my mom. I was wondering if you'd mind loaning me a few dollars till I get back on my feet?"

Now I understood. He had cleverly lead me to provide enough information to make me believe I'd once known him, then told a hard-luck story. It was a clever scam. I turned to him and grinned. "You're pretty good. You had me going there for a minute. I truly thought you had worked in my building."

A frown creased his face. "Man, I am down on my luck, though. And I'd sure appreciate some help.'

"I'm sorry but I don't give money to strangers on the street," I said.

The frown melted into lines of anger as his mouth turned down and his eyes hardened. He stalked away.

Two other times since that first, I'd been approached with much the same line. Now I wondered if this young woman's behavior was also a well-rehearsed scam.

Still, I gave her the benefit of the doubt and with my free hand I gave a friendly squeeze to her bare shoulder. Much too familiar a gesture I thought as I let go. "Listen, dear, I'm old enough to be your father—no grandfather. Why would you want to hang out with me?"

"I'm older than you think. People always think I'm younger."

"You certainly don't look a day over thirty - thirty-five."

She laughed and dismissed my comment with a wave of her hand. "I wish," she said and then followed up with, "Really, I'd like to go out with you sometime. Maybe dinner if not dancing." She stepped closer and when I gazed at her face I was reminded of another young woman who'd held me with the same liquid eyes and pleaded need.

It had happened years ago in the building at 6 N. Michigan where the Institute for Psychoanalysis had once resided. My friend, Jorge, and I had just had lunch and were standing at the elevators of the building, he getting ready to go upstairs to his office and I to leave for mine which was in the old Marshall Field's Annex building. A young, attractive woman dressed in what looked to be an expensive business suit came from out of the stairwell and approached us. She appeared somewhat dazed. Distraught. She held a Kleenex to one eye as she came up to us.

"Someone just stole my wallet," she said, a hiccupping sob escaping her.

"Oh, my gosh. When? Where?" I asked.

She turned her tear stained gaze on me and said, "I don't know. I had it when I was in the doctor's office but now it's gone. I don't know how I'm going to get home."

"That's terrible," said Jorge. "What are you going to do? Do you need to call someone?"

"I'm new to the city. I don't have anyone to call."

She took out another Kleenex and blew her nose. "I really need to get home. I've got some money there but not any now for train fare." She looked back and forth from Jorge to me and I felt as if I'd been cued to say something like, "Can I help you?" Jorge beat me to it.

"How much do you need to get home?"

"If you could give me a dollar, I can get the train," she said. "I'll be happy to repay you if you write down your name and address." She fished in her purse and pulled out a pen and piece of paper.

Jorge took a dollar bill from his billfold and handed it to her, waving away the proffered pen and paper.

"Oh, thank you, thank you. I don't know what I'd have done otherwise." With that, the young woman headed out the door and down Michigan in the direction I had to go.

"I think you just got scammed," I said.

Jorge's typical South American shrug pushed my doubts out the door behind the young lady. "Maybe. I don't think so."

DON'T BE FOOLISH, OLD MAN

"I'm going to follow her," I said. "I'll bet you a dollar to a hole in a doughnut she tries the same thing again."

Jorge just smiled, shook his head, and stepped into an elevator.

I walked briskly for the front door and, on exiting, saw the young woman half a block in front of me. I followed her as far as Washington and had she continued south, I would have abandoned my covert action and gone to my office at 25 E. Washington. But she turned west and when she came to a women's wear shop that was then at the northeast corner of Wabash and Washington, she entered one of the two front doors. Moments later, I followed her in. Once inside I could not see her because she had rounded a divider that separated the shop into two distinct sections, one for accessories and one for clothing. But I could hear her. And she was going through the same spiel she'd given Jorge and me.

I'd won my hole in a doughnut from Jorge, so why do anything more? Because I didn't like thinking she had gotten away with ripping off Jorge and was now using her sweet, helpless charms on someone else. Going up to a salesperson I told her a scam was taking place and she quickly turned on her heel and walked around the partition and said, "You, young lady. What do you think you're doing?"

"What do you mean?" the young scam artist said, pulling herself up to her full height. Then she saw me rounding the partition. I would swear her face turned white just before she whirled and dashing to the door, slammed through it and onto the sidewalk.

When I quickly exited after her, she was fleeing, running all-out west on Washington toward State Street. I had scared her into full flight.

I now wondered what the lovely young woman making a play for me here in the service station might be angling for.

"I said. "As I mentioned, I'm not out this way very often."

"That's okay. I work downtown." Sandra pulled a barrette from her hair and it cascaded down around her shoulders, a wave of black with what I noticed were a few ripples of silver.

"You do? Where?"

Raking her fingers through her hair she then tossed it back over her shoulders, exposing the smoothness of her skin. "Over by the post office. You can give me your phone number and I can call you and we can meet somewhere nearby."

Oh, sweet siren's song! If like Odysseus I could ask for a piece of bee's wax to plug my ears, or as he had commanded the ship's sailors to bind him to a mast, I could ask that my baser instincts be restrained. I had neither bee's wax nor sailors. Unlike Odysseus I'd had no previous warning that I would meet a siren and no one had warned me to guard against this lovely temptation standing so close to me I could smell the sweet scent of lavender. Now there was nothing to keep me from being swept up in this siren's music other than a strong inner voice inside me that kept repeating, "Don't give her your number." I ignored it.

"Sure. And you can give me yours," I said, hoping she would back away from doing that since I had not heeded my inner voice.

She quickly went to the cashier and borrowed a pen and wrote a phone number down then handed me the pen and paper. "Write down your phone number too," she said, handing me a second piece of paper.

"What's your last name, Sandra," I asked as I added her first name to the number.

"Oh, I'd rather not give that to you," she said. "Can't be too careful."

I laughed. "Now you're talking about being careful? You've not been very careful these last few minutes."

Sandra shrugged and said. "Now write down your number for me."

It was foolish of me, I realized immediately upon writing down my true number, but the situation had roused my egotism and immature fantasy that this improbable encounter held some gain for me. Or, I would like to think it was just because I am too trusting. As I finished writing down my number I teased, "I guess I'll just write my first name down as well. Like you said, one can't be too careful." That I was not being careful, I had no doubt even as I handed her the piece of paper to which I'd committed my name and number.

She only smiled at me and, taking the paper from me, said, "Thank you. I hope to see you soon." She then left with her cousin, only glancing back to smile encouragingly before letting the door close behind her.

I paid for my PAYDAY candy bar, got in my car, and ate it as I drove home. Unlike Sandra, at least the only scam this nutty, sweet thing would work on me was to begin a path to obesity.

I resisted the urge to dial the number Sandra gave me—or to answer the number when it showed up on my telephone screen, which it did twice. I did wonder what her scam would be if I called her or answered her call. "It would hurt nothing to explore this, would it?" I would ask myself, then answer. "Don't be foolish, old man."

DRIVING TO TANGO WITH SIRI

"Your destination is on your right," Siri tells me but I drive on past because all I see are motorcycle and car marquees at 617 South McClintock Avenue. There is no Argentine tango studio that I can see.

"Make a right at East Third Street and then turn right on South Perry Lane," Siri says sweetly but, paying no heed, I pull into a drive-in storage locker area, turn around and head back past where she first directed me. Though still being told by Siri that I've reached my destination, still see nothing resembling a dance studio so continue on toward University Drive.

"Proceed to the route," Siri commands in a less sweet tone.

I pull into the Minder Binder Restaurant's parking lot, wheel around and "proceed to the route." It's at times like this that I really do miss having a real live companion to help direct me. And to dance with.

"Your destination is on your right," Siri tells me again.

There is absolutely nothing resembling a dance studio on my right. Feeling extremely peevish yet a fool for reacting to a robot, I say aloud to Siri, "You don't give very good directions."

"I don't want to argue," she replies in a tone my high school math teacher used when faced with some obstreperous and rebellious comment from me.

I don't want to argue either, so I shut up and turn into the drive fronting the vehicular enterprises and "proceed" to the alley. There is no tango studio that I can see, and I'm getting really frustrated with Siri. I swing around, drive back toward McClintock and as I pass motorcycles behind plate glass windows, Siri pipes up and says,

"You have reached your destination."

Holding down the button on the phone I retort, "Not unless I want to tango with a Harley,."

"I don't believe I understand," responds Siri.

I shut my phone off. "So there, Siri," I think.

I really want to have an opportunity to perhaps meet a dance companion at the tango lesson and also to have a lesson with David Lui, one of the teachers in the Phoenix area whom I really enjoy and admire, otherwise I think I might just go home. On a previous evening Siri had unerringly guided me to another ballroom where I took a group lesson before the general dancing begins. That lesson had been billed as Argentine tango but turned out to be some type of advance showmanship tango moves much too complicated for a beginners class. The young instructor was Romanian, had just purchased the ballroom, and I suspected was trying to make an impression. With me he did—a poor impression.

Later that same evening, during the ball while dancing waltz and fox trot, I met two women dancers who invited me to a Milonga, one I was unfamiliar with that was located in Scottsdale. It roused my hope that

DRIVING TO TANGO WITH SIRI

I might connect with a regular partner and so I set out with Siri who (or is it which?) took me to that Milonga without a hitch. There I found the two ladies I'd met at the ballroom dance who were there with about twenty-five other individuals, all of whom knew one another and had been dancing together for fifteen-plus years. There were more men than women and knowing the women, they quickly found a partner. Being a stranger, I did not immediately find anyone to dance with other than the two who had invited me. I danced one tango with each soon after I'd arrived and before they chose someone else. These dancers had learned a different style of Argentine tango than I knew, and had become cliquish in the many years they'd danced together. I'd left early, disappointed that I'd not found anyone I could hope would be a regular partner but happy that at least Siri remained friendly and guided me back home safely.

After that disappointing experience, I am not going to miss tonight's opportunity to meet someone and to have a lesson with David even if I was late. So I drive back to the Minder Binder Restaurant parking lot, where I park and walk down what looks to be more an alley than the walkway to a restaurant's entrance. A motorcycle sits outside the door. Loud music I don't like is playing over the sound system's cranked-up speakers. I can barely hear the waiter's reply when he answers my question, "Where is 617?"

"Next door," he says, never taking his eyes off the television where the Phoenix Suns are struggling to keep up with some team from back East.

No longer trusting Siri, I walk "next door" where I still can see only motorcycle and auto stores, and repair shops. I'm ready to grind my teeth. It's getting much too late.

I call my niece, who calls the studio, and someone there tells her, "Yes, we are at 617. Next door to Minder Binder."

I get back to my car, turn on my phone and invite Siri to once more guide me. She remains quiet until I slowly drive back into the driveway lined with stores selling or servicing what many red-blooded American men crave, cars and motorcycles. Most of those men wouldn't be caught dead in a tango class, so why would, I wonder, Siri, the café waiter, and my niece all guide me here?

Siri pipes up once more, "You have reached your destination," and as if magically materializing from out of nowhere, I spot a sign clearly spelling out Tango Center. The narrow entrance is squeezed between two of the he-man stores' entrances and I should have seen it before now—paid attention to my trusty friend, Siri, that I had reached my destination.

The tension in my shoulders relaxes and on my iPhone, I summon Siri and I apologize for not paying closer attention to her directions. "No need to apologize," she says and I think, this is getting ridiculous.

I enter and see David, who has begun the class, and eight other students grouped closely about him. An older woman, Nancy, not present in the other lessons I'd had with David, stands nearby. I'd seen him with her on Facebook, the two of them demonstrating dozens of tango steps. Both are about five feet four and of some Latin extraction and both have an easy, sweet smile. They are huggers, and welcome even a stranger with close embraces. Their style of dance is done in a close embrace, chest to chest, though they show many steps where dancers have to move apart. She looks old enough to be his mother, and, as I soon learn, is his mother. She's let her graying blond hair hang loose and it reaches her waist. She wears a loose-fitting, colorful, unpatterned skirt and white blouse; David sports a faintly visible five-o'clock mustache and trimmed goatee and is dressed in black slacks and a white shirt.

The five other women and three men turn to look at me; there are nearly always more women than men who show up to dance lessons. Most men, not believing dancing to be a manly thing to do, never learn how manly and physical it can be. I don't see any sissies in this group. When in a previous class David asked if any of us had ever engaged in sports, one of the group here tonight, Donald, told us that he was into martial arts. And four decades earlier, in the day when I might have considered dancing unmanly, I'd earned a black belt in judo.

One couple present is young and obviously "a twosome" but the other students have come alone. There's Joe who looks like an Indian Scout from out of a fifties' cowboy movie, and is as earnest and focused as the woman with him is intensely taciturn. Both smile infrequently. The only other man, Mark, is young, tall and dark and across his cheeks and jaws is a week-old, six o'clock shadow. Two other women are in their late fifties to early seventies. Dressed in a black pants suit, and with dark hair cut short, Trish is slim and moves with cat-like grace. Slender Patricia, looking something like a china doll, wears a fashionable dress that accentuates her well-molded body. Both women have unlined faces that speak to excellent facial surgery, which Hilda's, another tall woman, lined face has never known. Past seventy, Hilda is not petite, but rather solid. She and Trish are quick to smile or laugh, but Patricia is solemn as a nun. The young couple who are in their late twenties and obviously smitten with one another listen closely to David but frequently glance lovingly in one another's direction and smile like lovers in a romance movie.

Then there is me, old enough to be the father or grandfather of all but Hilda, who, none-the-less has to be ten years younger than me. My short-sleeved, blue-and-tan shirt, the patterned colors dabbed here and there in random fashion, is like a modern art piece. I've also worn plain blue trousers but with cuffs; I've had them for ten years at least and the cuffs date me as much or more than my wrinkles. I have on my soft, clunky walking shoes which give even more the impression of an elderly gentleman whose feet hurt. Well, they do. A lot. They would hurt more, I'm convinced, if

I didn't dance and do strengthening exercises for the foot muscles. And I pad the bottoms of my dance shoes which I immediately don. Two hair transplants have only managed to cover the front part of my balding head and I have to part my hair lower than I'd like to cover the gap between the sides and top of my skull. If I thought I had another ten or fifteen years ahead of me, I'd be tempted to have a third transplant. Fill in the gaps. My mother had brown eyes and my dad blue, but genetics decreed that both my sister and I end up with blue eyes.

When I visited Arizona a year ago, something I've done for the past twenty-seven years, on a whim, I took my first tango lesson. From David. And now I'm back a year later with twelve months of frequent tango lessons with Fred and a few with Paola, Eduardo, Daniela, and Hernan. I spent two weeks in Buenos Aries and danced almost every day, taking lessons or going to Milongas. I've just lately been labeled by a private tango instructor, Paola, an Argentine woman, a beginning intermediate-level dancer. I think she's overoptimistic. She spent the first ten lessons just teaching me how to tango walk. She told me that when she first learned to tango in Argentina, her teacher would let her do nothing but walk for the first year. She cheered when he taught her the first additional tango step. I cheered when she stopped insisting we do nothing but tango walk—she seemed to want me to be a national contender but I only wanted to be a social dancer.

I want to go out almost every night to dance ballroom or tango. There are a number of Argentine tango venues in the area and people in them vary their style of dance from the formal, technically correct to the informal, passionate, "from the heart" tango that focuses more on the relationship with the music and the partner than on technique. For a relatively new beginner like me, it is confusing at times as I try to navigate around a dance floor with women who have

DRIVING TO TANGO WITH SIRI

different expectations of me as their partner. There are fifteen styles of tango that have evolved since the dance first came on the scene a hundred years ago. I like David's style, I'm really not sure what it could be labeled, so while visiting Tempe, I don't miss a lesson with him even though he does not sponsor Milongas.

Learning tango is not easy. David puts into words how difficult it is when he tells the class that "the first year for women is easy because all they have to do is follow the lead of the man. For the man, the first year is very hard because they not only have to learn all the steps and how to lead them, but also to concentrate on their tango posture and how to dissociate." (I learned in my psychiatry residency that to dissociate was to detach the mind from an emotional state or even from the body, that dissociation is characterized by a sense of the world as a dreamlike or unreal place and may be accompanied by poor memory of specific events. In tango, dissociation is to turn one's upper body from side to side without also turning the hips. If you are a ballroom dancer, try this. It's hard to do.) David goes on to say, "But in the second year it is much harder for the women. They must begin to add to the dance, learn how to overcome the mistakes of the man and keep dancing. It takes two years before both the men and the women are comfortable enough to do tango." I was a year away from being comfortable. When I first began a year ago, I was told by one purist instructor that he'd never heard of an eighty-two-year-old man who tried to learn tango and he implied that he was skeptical I could learn. Throughout my life when I've been told that I'm not capable of doing something it has motivated me to work all the harder to do so. And most times I've succeeded. So here I am a year later and, though aware it takes even more than two years to begin to really feel like a good tango dancer, I'm hanging in.

When I join the group, David demonstrates an easy step for the benefit of the beginners in the class and though I've been told I have intermediate skills, I take this beginner's class to solidify what I already know. And it's a good way to get to know people. I suspect, too, that dancing with those of less skill than me makes me feel more secure, but I wouldn't want anyone to know that. And as the lesson progresses, I do get to know four of the women better and to feel more confident.

Trish has been taking tango lessons for two months. She has a perfect frame and what she knows she dances well. She looks into my eyes without any self-consciousness and with such tango passion that it's hard to hold her gaze.

This is Hilda's first lesson. She struggles with imitating what David shows us to do, but she persists. She obviously is enjoying herself—and me. She apologizes for her mistakes a couple of times, and I tell her there is no apologizing in tango. "Besides," I tell her, "50 percent of the mistakes you make are the man's fault and the other 50 percent aren't yours." She laughs at the absurdity of my remark.

Patricia doesn't say how long she's been taking lessons but it's soon clear she is way past beginner's level. She dances as she looks, like a China doll. I'm afraid I will break her, she is so delicate. But, at the same time, I feel a distancing and brittleness about her. She's quick to let me know how I can correct a mistake. And not kindly. I can manage to overlook her critical attitude though her standoffishness makes me uneasy.

The fourth lady, the one paired with the Indian fighter, follows well but seems to quickly gravitate back to her partner with whom she spends most of the lesson.

David goes from couple to couple pointing out ways to correct a move. Just a slight turn of the foot, or turning on a heel instead of a toe, or sometimes a toe instead of a heel, makes a world of difference in the execution of a tango step. Loose arms sink good tango leads just as during the Second World War it was said that loose lips sank ships. One of the hardest lessons to learn when it comes to one's frame is to keep the arms from flapping about. They must be strong and give clear signals to the partner. David sees these things, and lets his students know in ways that are kind and supportive. No hint of criticism. He demonstrates moves with the other women or with his mother whom, halfway through the lesson, he calls, "Mom." It was then that I understand this is a mother-son team. At the end of the first hour we all take a break and dance to music David has left on.

Fifteen minutes later we will begin the intermediate/advanced class. The level of complexity of the tango steps will increase. David will be patient. He breaks things down and shows how one move of the body flows into a move of the feet. In my previous lesson on Tuesday he'd asked if there were any questions or concerns and I'd said, "I have so much trouble keeping in mind these steps after I've seemed to learn them. How does one learn and maintain all this knowledge?"

David then spoke of how he taught. "It's important to learn each element of a step, to repeat it over and over again before going to the next element. Then those two elements together must be practiced over and over before the next element is introduced. And so on until you have the entire step memorized."

I say to myself, "And then I must go over and over that complete step a hundred times for it to stick in my head."

I played first chair trombone in high school and could not read a lick of music. I can learn complicated tango steps and not be able to call their names. And as I've grown older, the steps I learn in class and can do well also escape memory as the hours pass. Vals, milonga, boleo, paso, salida, freno, adorno, gancho, giro, lustrada, molinete, cruzada, ocho, parada, parallel system, cross system; I could go on with dozens more terms. These I list are some of the basic ones. Their meaning sometimes escapes me when I most need them; when the instructor using the term tells the class we should perform one of them. If I could immediately assign the names to steps, I could better remember how to do them, but they just won't stick—or I just have some deep-seated resistance to allowing myself to remember things. Or, do I have a learning disability? I suppose that's possible. I just know that I have to really discipline myself to study the names of the steps if I want to master the skill of tango dancing. I say this to one of the women I'm dancing with who says, "I can't remember the names of the steps either. But I don't worry about it. I just follow my partner's lead."

I ask Trish to dance as we await the second lesson and lead her as best I can using the steps we went over in the beginners' class. She gives me a tip on how I can signal her for one of the steps, the name of which I can't remember. I enjoy dancing with her. I do know some of the steps, and I do a good tango walk. Several women have commented on that fact.

The second lesson is even more difficult than the first because it involves dance moves that test the strength of my legs and my ability to pivot 180 degrees while keeping my balance. By the end of class I've learned to better execute the steps, whatever they are, and I'm exhausted. And hungry. I've not had dinner. I don't want to eat alone, so ask Hilda, who has tarried as the others quickly left, if she'd like to have something to eat with me. She says, "Yes."

We change our shoes, walk over to the Minder Binder and have a quick meal before the evening comes to a close. She'd led an interesting early life and is an interesting person, so I invite her to have another tango lesson with me next evening, but she lets me know she is in a relationship.

It will be only Siri and me driving to have a "group lesson" at the Tango Argentine the next evening.

Siri and I are together for a very long time as we wind our way past malls and housing developments. She guides me unerringly to the address I gave her, but it takes me a few minutes of driving around the large shopping complex to find the right building. Once located, I find myself in front of a fitness club where several young, sweating females mill about in the general area. On one side is a nail salon and on the other a women's clothing store. Somehow it seems a more appropriate location than one squashed between stores selling macho-wheeled, metal conveyances.

Online I'd read about Tango Argentine. "Every Thursday the Intermediate level emphasize on musicality, interaction, and communication between partners, the intention of the dance. Authentic Argentine Tango, Milonga, Candombe, and Vals Cruzado" is taught exclusively by Argentine Teachers." It sounded impressive despite the awkward English. But I thought, hey, you don't have to speak or write good English to teach Tango. Even Siri, with all her computer genius, mispronounced words sometimes.

Once inside the workout establishment, I ask about the tango lesson from a lady at the front desk and am told she isn't sure but thinks it is in one of the workout rooms. I find nothing resembling a tango class in either of the three smaller rooms she pointed toward so I sit in the waiting area, change into my dance shoes and—wait.

At precisely eight o'clock one very large, I might say corpulent man with long, greasy hair, stalks into the lobby and grunts, "tango" as he passes through the waiting area. Without waiting for a response, he leads me and two others, Dan and Janie, into a room large enough for a small yoga class. Without introducing himself he asks me how long I've been taking tango lessons, and when I say "a year" he motions to the woman and says, "Dance with her so I can get some sense of how much you know." I look questioningly at the husband who smiles and nods. The instructor watches as I dance my meager repertoire of dance steps with the woman who had immediately said, "I'm just a beginner," and then, every time she missteps or I give her a poor lead, apologizes, even after I repeatedly tell her there is never a reason to apologize, and trot out the same words I'd spoken to Hilda the night before—50 percent of the mistakes a couple make are the man's doing and the other 50 percent are not the woman's fault. Her worried look disappears and she smiles, her ordinary face showing a flash of momentary attractiveness.

At the end of the dance, the instructor says to me, "The first thing you have to do is stop ballroom dancing. Ja?" He strikes the exaggerated pose of a ballroom dance frame. "This is not for tango!" He reaches for the woman, pulls her in close, and wraps his long, heavy arm about her as he leans forward. "Tango is a passionate dance. A dance where two people are getting to know one another. It's a conversation without words but an intimate one. You can't dance it if you look off into the distance. Ja?" Then he steps away and asks, "What is the most important thing about Argentine tango?"

"The relationship?" I hazard.

"No!" he shouts. "It is the music. The music is tango. Tango is the music. You must relate first to the music before you can dance. All the fancy steps you see make no difference. Ja? It's how the music is felt and expressed. That's tango. Ja?"

As he has answered his own questions by the repeated, "Ja," I let pass any response to them. When I was a child, during the Second World War, I watched scores of movies where German soldiers would punctuate their interactions with prisoners with the word, "Ja," so I decide that not yet knowing the instructor's name I will think of him as the "The Fat German."

I think back to what three other tango teachers had taught me that was contrary to what I am now hearing and decide that, for this one lesson, I will dance The Fat German's way—and try to get into a more passionate mood of dancing even though I may again have the other man's wife in my arms.

Finishing with me, he has the husband, Dan, dance with Janie and as I watch him bully Dan, I wonder if this strange tango teacher's father had been one of the Germans who fled to Argentina when the Second World War was over.

I have two more dances with Janie before the lesson concludes and feel we both are a bit bruised by the experience. I think about making excuses and leaving but don't want to abandon the couple to the exclusive attention of The Fat German though, strangely, I feel sorry for him. I sense a vulnerability behind the forced bravado with which he attacks the tango lesson. He is trying too hard. I am relieved, though, when the hour lesson is up. After taking my twenty dollars for the lesson, way too much to ask for a group lesson, he says to me, "You are a good student. Ja? You take instructions and follow them very well. You will come back, ja?"

"Thanks," I say, choking back a retort on the tip of my tongue. I almost blurt out, "Ja wohl, Herr Kommandant." Instead I tell him I live in Chicago.

He goes on to ask if I will write a comment on Facebook recommending his lesson and though I only give a half-hearted nod, he writes out his online address. He says "You write something, ja," and thrusts the piece of paper into my hand.

I don't respond, "Ja" but neither do I say, "Nein."

Though feeling lonely and wishing I had a regular dance partner to share my tango experiences, I am happy to have Siri keep me company and show me the way on the forty-five-minute drive home. I only wish she could tango. On impulse I ask her, "Siri, do you tango dance?"

"No, but I do a pretty mean robot," she says.

TWO ANGELS
IN THE NIGHT

I looked forward with some trepidation to a Saturday evening that I was spending with a Jungian analyst, whom I'll call Edith, the two of us having been invited weeks before by mutual friends to their home for dinner. At the time I was invited, it did not occur to me that the dinner was just two days before the first anniversary of the loss of my wife, Carolyn. I had some suspicion that this dinner was my hostess's attempt at matchmaking and that was part of my discomfort. I was not quite ready to pursue any intimate, serious relationship. Carolyn was too much on my mind.

There was a period of sadness in the dinner group as we discovered that the hostess's father had passed away only two weeks previously and that I was dealing with the one-year anniversary of my wife, Carolyn's, death. Though it sobered the group somewhat we continued on with our evening and did not let thoughts of death linger.

Later that evening, after a wonderful dinner, Edith and I said our goodnights and left. Upon reaching the street, she took hold of my arm and invited me to walk with her, so we strolled over to, and then down, Michigan Avenue. Around 10:45 P.M., we said our goodbyes, she hailing a cab and me walking on down Michigan Avenue toward my apartment.

There were hundreds of people on Michigan Avenue, a stark change from fifty-six years earlier when I'd first come to Chicago. Then, this part of the city was almost deserted; I might see at most only ten or fifteen people hurrying on their way to get off the street. This crowd strolled leisurely down the sidewalk. It would have been no surprise to find that over half of those I now saw were tourists. I enjoy people-watching and was in no hurry to get home. Carolyn was on my mind as I strolled and I knew she would have enjoyed this leisurely pace and the people-watching.

I'd had no idea of how long a walk I'd be taking this lovely, warm evening, so had not donned my walking shoes. I had to saunter along on aching feet and when I saunter, I place my hands behind my back and must look like an aging college professor in deep thought as he strolls across a university campus. Too, I was probably the only one out of those hundreds on the street who was dressed in slacks, subdued blue shirt, and a comfortable sports jacket, all which I'd purchased the year before while visiting Buenos Aries. Like a professor, I was deep in my own thoughts when, a block from home, two young, attractive women came up to me and asked, "Do you live around here?"

Thinking they were tourists from out of town and perhaps unsure where they were or how to get to some destination, I answered, "Yes. How can I help you?"

"Oh, we don't need help,' said one who later told me her name was Kindra.

TWO ANGELS IN THE NIGHT

It was difficult for me not to notice that Kindra was dressed, as were most of the young women on the street that night, in shorts, which showed off shapely legs, and a shortened top that revealed an ample midriff. Her blond hair was well-styled and she had an open, friendly smile on her face as she made very good eye contact with me. In the subdued glow of the street lights I could not see their color.

"We just passed you a moment ago and decided to turn back and speak to you," said the other similarly dressed young woman, Samantha, as she also later told me. Her long hair fell about her shoulders and she had a large tattoo on her right arm and shoulder.

The tattoo distracted me for a moment as I can't seem to shake the bias I have against such permanent adornment of the beautiful skin of the younger generation. Fifty-five years ago, when I encountered anyone sporting tattoos in the Veterans Hospital where I did my psychiatry residency, they were almost invariably either a former sailor or a psychopath, or both. This young lady did not look like a sailor but she could well be a psychopath. I didn't know for sure, though, so I tried to stifle my bias because she had such an open, friendly demeanor. I noticed that she deferred to Kindra who took the lead in our further conversation. I was wary, though, my thought about the psychopaths and other troublesome characters I'd met in my lifetime made me wonder why these young ladies would so boldly approach me on the street.

"Oh," I said at a loss of anything else to say. Some might advise that what I should have said was, "excuse me," and then walked on. That's not my nature.

"You said you lived around here?" Kindra said.

"Why yes. Just around the corner here on Lake Street. But why did you decide to speak to me?"

"We talked to some other guy earlier and he was really creepy," said Samantha, not answering the real question of why they would be approaching strangers on the street.

Two other times in my life I had been approached by a pair of young ladies that first engaged me in friendly conversation which led to them offering services I've never been inclined to engage. I couldn't help but wonder if they would be asking me at any moment, "Want to party?" Or, could they be setting me up for one of them to pickpocket me? I put a hand protectively over my wallet. Or could they be working with some male counterpart who would mug me? Or, Or. Or. So many possibilities. But, feeling mellow and safe amid all the tourists and residents walking the street, I decided to relax and wait to find out what would happen. The liquor and wine I'd had at dinner had long since ceased to affect me so I couldn't blame my decision on that. Let's just say I was curious and let it go at that. Still, I was a little nonverbal, apparently having used up all my clever conversation earlier in the evening. I rejoined the conversation with a reserved, "Hmm."

"Yeah," added Kindra, "but you looked interesting."

Recovering my wits somewhat I asked, "But what brings you out to this neighborhood so late?"

"We decided we would pretend to be tourists tonight and walk from home to Navy Pier and back. We didn't quite make it to Navy Pier, though."

"So, you live close by?" I asked.

"In the South Loop," said Samantha. "Oh, and by the way, what is your accent?"

"Southwestern. I'm from Oklahoma. I'm a cowboy."

They both laughed and then Samantha said, "My mother is from Oklahoma."

"I probably wouldn't know her," I said and they both laughed again.

I believe it was Samantha that asked, "Is it okay if I ask your age?"

I really have accepted that I am no longer a young man and that it shows in my face though I treasure my posture which has not yet declined into an old man's stoop. "Sure, it's okay," I said, "I'm eighty-six-years-old."

"You are?" asked Kindra, some incredulity slipping into her voice. "I thought you were probably in your"—here there was a pause as I suspect she was trying to make her guesstimate palatable to me,—"seventies."

Samantha echoed her companion's disclaimer with, "Yes, you really don't look like you're eighty-six."

"Why thank you," I said, not adding that at any age it would be pleasant to speak with two lovely women who complimented me.

So, we let the subject of age drop there and Kindra asked again, "Where did you say you lived?"

Abandoning my better judgement, I said, "Just around the corner on Lake Street."

"May we walk you home?" chimed in Samantha.

In for a penny, in for a dime. But I wouldn't invite them up. "Sure. But you don't have to."

"But we'd like to," said Kindra.

"I don't even know your names," I said, and at that point they both introduced themselves and put out a hand for me to shake. After saying, "My name is Cliff," I took each of their hands which were soft though strong in grip.

We trouped off together to the front of my building, Samantha and Kindra chatting away about where they worked. Samantha was a waitress and Kindra the night manager of a nice restaurant in the South Loop. They asked if I'd ever heard of it. I hadn't. They both assured me it had wonderful food and that I had to come and visit it. "I'll see that you get a free meal," Kindra said. All the way to my apartment building I wondered what they actually had in mind. Were they going to offer a proposition once we reached my building? Finally ask if I wanted to party?

On reaching the building's front door I stopped and said, "It's been really nice talking to the two of you," or something inane like that. I'd come to believe there were no accomplices, the front of building was well-lighted and there were multitudes of people even on my quiet street. And they had not wanted to come up and party. They actually seemed like two very nice, young women who were being "appropriately" nice to me.

They both assured me that they'd really loved talking to me. Kindra wanted me to take her phone number and email so I could contact her, and she could arrange for me to have a free dinner during an evening when she was on duty. Samantha said she wanted to make sure that she was my waitress.

I stood there, looking from one to the other, still not absolutely sure what was going on with them though I was beginning to think they really were just two young women looking for some safe male to treat them halfway decently and without sexual intent, even though they exuded youth and sensuality. They confirmed this, I believe, as they readied to depart. First Kindra and then Samantha asked if I would give them a hug.

Why not? I thought. Hugs are free and don't obligate one. And they were two lovely and huggable young ladies. I gave each a bear hug which they returned and then they walked on down the street leaving me feeling much better but a little guilty that I'd doubted their motives. Mostly, though, I felt as if I'd entertained two granddaughters who themselves needed a hug before they went on their way to further adventures, whatever that was to be. I just hoped they didn't run into any more creeps.

I was happy for them that they were two ladies in the night and not two ladies of the night.

The next morning, I told a slightly older and somewhat more worldly-wise friend of mine, Nichole, my American ballroom dance instructor, about the incident and, knowing it was only a day before the anniversary of Carolyn's passing, she said something very sweet to me.

"I don't know if you believe in this sort of thing or not, but it makes me wonder if maybe it could have been Carolyn reaching down from wherever she is and giving you hugs. Or maybe she sent two angels to do it for her?"

True, I don't believe in those kinds of things but I found her words comforting. Also, comforting was the hug of compassion Nichole then gave me.

Hey! Hugs are free and nonbinding. And dancers for the most part are huggers.

I wondered if Kindra and Samantha were dancers.

Or some manifestation of Carolyn?

Or earthly angels?

AUTHOR BIO

Cliff Wilkerson is a retired child, adolescent, and adult psychoanalyst and psychiatrist who now spends his time visiting with friends and family, reading, writing, teaching, traveling, ballroom dancing, and learning to Argentine tango. He has published three previous books, *Beautiful Brown Eyes*, *Moving On*, and *Still Moving On*. He lives with his memories in downtown Chicago where he can walk in Millennium Park, stroll along the Riverwalk or the shores of Lake Michigan, and visit scores of interesting places to dine.